Classic English Folk Songs

Selected and Edited by R. Vaughan Williams and A. L. Lloyd

Revised by Malcolm Douglas

Classic English Folk Songs

Selected and Edited by R. Vaughan Williams and A. L. Lloyd

Revised by Malcolm Douglas

Foreword by Martin Carthy

Published by The English Folk Dance & Song Society
in association with The South Riding Folk Network

2003

Published by the English Folk Dance & Song Society
in association with The South Riding Folk Network

EFDSS, Cecil Sharp House, 2 Regent's Park Road, London, NW1 7AY, United Kingdom

First published 2003

British Library Cataloguing in Publication Data
Data available

ISBN 0 85418 188 1

1 3 5 7 9 10 8 6 4 2

Designed and typeset in Perpetua by Wheeler & Porter Ltd
Music setting by Julian Elloway
Publishing Consultants Nigel Lynn Publishing & Marketing Ltd
Printed in the United Kingdom
on acid-free paper by
Antony Rowe Ltd., Chippenham

Contents

PREFACES

I am so pleased that the Penguin Book of English Folk Songs has been reissued under the auspices of the English Folk Dance and Song Society. It was the last publication with which my husband was associated before his death in 1958 and it is most appropriate that it should appear in 2003, the centenary of both Cecil Sharp's and Vaughan Williams's first forays into folk song collecting. I hope that a new generation will gain a lifetime's pleasure from these beautiful songs which might so easily have been lost to us if it had not been for the splendid work of those devoted pioneers.

Ursula Vaughan Williams

I have an image in my mind of Ralph Vaughan Williams and my dad, A. L. Lloyd, in the sitting room of our house in Greenwich many years ago. Vaughan Williams is sitting very still by an open door leading out into the garden, and dad is busily moving around with a secret smile sorting papers into piles on a table. There is a quiet air of excitement. The reason why this image has remained so vivid is because it was lovely to be there in the room with them. They seemed delighted to be putting together the material for publication so that other people could enjoy it as much as they did. My mother and I are very pleased that the English Folk Dance and Song Society are making sure that another generation has access to their book.

Caroline Clayton

FOREWORD

This is a long awaited and very welcome reprint. Ralph Vaughan Williams died before plans for the original *Penguin Book of English Folk Songs* could come to fruition, the final preparation being placed in the equally adventurous hands of A. L. 'Bert' Lloyd for its eventual publication in 1959. And because this collection was such a long way ahead of its time, it has stood up so well over the years.

This was, of course, the first time that something even remotely resembling what might, with considerable trepidation, be called 'the real thing', had been made available in a publication specifically aimed at the general public. Earlier collections served up a meal which gravitated towards the sweet. Here in the *Penguin Book* one was given fibre. Spine. Gristle, even. A banquet, nonetheless. Truly, these are the extraordinary musical creations of ordinary people, often created out of thin air. That is what Folk Music is. And one has the impression that the mediating hand is exerting a far lighter touch than in hitherto not-so-bold collections. Which is not to say that life herein is not opinionated. Far from it. But the choices were bold, better to demonstrate the sheer diversity of this music, with sets of words being completed where the editors thought necessary. The musical language may on occasion (and certainly to 1959 ears) have seemed a little odd. But it was, and is, uniquely English. This music is not easy, but why on earth should it be? That, after all, is what makes it interesting. The people who made these songs were not noble savages and incompetent, but sophisticated musicians who knew what they were doing (the same holds true today).

The *Penguin* selection raids a far wider set of sources and names many collectors. Cecil Sharp's highly mediated selections from his own vast collection had been out of print and unavailable for several years. Likewise those edited by Lucy Broadwood and The Reverend Sabine Baring-Gould. Certainly the time had come to look again, this time trusting ordinary people a little more with what is, after all, their very own musical heritage. This was the outstanding result.

Martin Carthy

INTRODUCTION

AN old Suffolk labourer with a fine folk song repertory and a delicate, rather gnat-like voice, once remarked: 'I used to be reckoned a good singer before these here *tunes* came in.' The *tunes* he spoke of with such scorn had come in with a vengeance, and it seemed that his kind of songs, once so admired, would be lost under the flood of commercial popular music. However, folk songs are tough, and show an obstinate will to survive. Of recent years, they have begun to reassert themselves in places where formerly only *tunes* were heard, and now it seems that many young people, whose musical nourishment had been limited to whatever came to them in canned form from the Charing Cross Road, are looking to folk music for something that they can take and re-make as their own. The ceilidh, the folk-singing party, is becoming a part of urban social life, and the voice of the revival folk-singer makes itself heard in youth hostels, city pubs, skiffle cellars, even in jazz clubs. It is a curious but welcome phenomenon, this revival of folk music as a city music. It seems that many taking part in that revival have come to appreciate British balladry through their interest in jazz. A search for the roots of jazz leads to American folk song, and a search for the origins of American folk song leads the astonished enthusiast back home to his own traditional music. It is to the partisans of the new folk song revival that this book is first addressed, but we hope, too, that our selection will contain some delightful surprises for those who have been singing folk songs for years.

The songs we have chosen are all taken from the *Journal of the Folk Song Society* and its continuation, the *Journal of the English Folk Dance and Song Society*. The Folk Song Society was founded in 1898, as the culmination of the work of Baring-Gould, Lucy Broadwood, Fuller Maitland, Frank Kidson, and others in rescuing the beautiful traditional music of England from oblivion. The Folk Song Society and its successor, the English Folk Dance and Song Society, have published annually, as their *Journal*, a small volume of the songs discovered by their members. Many of the songs have found their way to a wide public, being printed in settings for voice and piano, for choir, or in other forms. We have included none of these in the present volume, but have confined ourselves to songs and variants unpublished outside the pages of the *Journals*. Thus, this book consists of versions of songs that have hitherto remained in what is practically a private collection. We have found our choice hard to make, for in this book we have room for only a small portion of the two thousand or so British traditional melodies contained in the *Journals*. Reluctantly, we decided to leave out all occupational and seasonal songs, such as Christmas carols, harvest songs, and sailors' shanties. These may be included in a future volume.

This is a book to sing from. To make the songs singable, the editorial hand has been used where necessary. We assure our readers that the melodies have not been doctored, but are as the collector took them from the traditional singer. With the words, the case is rather different. Music is a matter of emotion, words of logic. If a bad singer mars a tune, we either keep it as it is, or leave it out; in no case do we alter it. However, if a forgetful singer omits verses or lines, or knows the song only in imperfect form, we do not hesitate, in compiling a book for popular use, to complete the song from other traditional sources. Phillips Barry, a responsible American folk song scholar, speaks for us: 'Different obligations bind the maker of a scientific work to be thrown to the lions of scholarship and the maker of a practical work for people who like singing... The editor of a practical work has the right and is under the duty to make both singable and understandable the song he edits... Both singer and scholar, nevertheless, into whose hands the book may fall, have today a right... to know both the extent and the sources of editorial changes and restorations.'

Accordingly, in several instances we have collated various versions of song-texts, whether recorded from oral sources or printed on broadsides. Where we have done this, we say so in our Notes, and we give the source of our borrowing. In very rare cases, and only where it seemed otherwise very hard to make the text fit the tune, we have ventured to cancel a few words, or to add interjections such as 'oh' or 'and', in order to complete the scansion of a line. In most cases, irregular lines have been left irregular, for therein lies some of the beauty of folk song; any folk singer worth his salt delights in variation, and some of the happiest rhythmical effects may come from making the tune fit the words instead of adapting the text to the tune.

In a few cases, we have shortened songs that seemed overlong for what they had to say. On the other hand, we have not hesitated to include words, verses, or whole texts which earlier collectors prudishly modified or omitted as being objectionable. The old habit of cleaning-up or even entirely re-writing the texts led to the false supposition that folk songs are always 'quite nice'. The folk singer has no objection to plain speech. He is likely to be forthright in his treatment of the pleasures and pains of love, though he may class some songs as 'outway rude' which we think quite harmless. In restoring song-texts that had hitherto been published only in bowdlerised form, we have referred to the collectors' original manuscripts.

We have said that the melodies represent the songs as the collectors reported them. The remark needs some qualification. In a few cases the *Journal* versions showed errors of musical grammar, and these have been corrected. One or two tunes needed re-barring. Several of the melodies have been transposed, in the interests of orderliness and singability. Otherwise, we have been at pains to preserve the collectors' impression of what their informants were actually singing. It must be confessed that when, perhaps under the influence of modern convention, a singer has weakened certain phrases of a fine modal tune, the temptation to 'correct' his singing is great. We have resisted that temptation. In one instance, however, it may be considered that we have cheated slightly. The singer of No. 29, *The Grey Cock*, constantly sang a final F on the recording. Her son remembers that she used to sing a final D. The D preserves the modal character of this beautiful tune, whereas the F comes as a disappointment. In our transcription we have retained the D, but have indicated the F as a variant.

We would like to give a few suggestions for singing the songs in this book. The ideal way to sing an English folk song, of course, is unaccompanied. Our melodies were made to be sung that way, and much of their tonal beauty and delightful suppleness comes from the fact that they have been traditionally free from harmonic or rhythmic accompaniment. They are best suited to stand on their own, and we rather agree with the Dorset countryman who commented on a professional singer of folk songs: 'Of course, it's nice for him to have the piano when he's singing, but it does make it very awkward for the listener.'

However, for those to whom the unaccompanied voice seems naked, there is no harm in adding a few supporting chords on the pianoforte, guitar, or other instrument, provided the chords are in keeping with the style of the tune. Special care needs to be taken when accompanying modal tunes, where the chords should be strictly in the mode. As to which instruments should or should not be used for folk song accompaniment, this is entirely a matter of choice. The fashionable guitar has no more traditional sanction that the less fashionable pianoforte. The concertina, mouth-organ, fiddle, banjo, zither, spoons, bones, even the harmonium have all been used as accompaniment to country singers without necessarily resulting in a performance that sounds more 'right' than that given by the voice unadorned. On pages xxi and xxii we print a few examples of the way in which, in our opinion, the songs might be harmonized. But we hope that our readers will sing the songs unaccompanied as much as possible.

It should not be necessary to impress on our readers that this volume does not offer them what is mere clownish nonsense or only of antiquarian interest. Béla Bartók, who knew more about folk music than any other musician of our time, once said: 'Folk melodies are a real model of the highest artistic perfection. To my mind, on a small scale, they are masterpieces just as much as, in the world of larger forms, a fugue by Bach or a Mozart sonata.' We believe that the songs in this book are not only full of classical beauty, but are the foundations on which all more matured musical art must be built. This has been recognized in every country except England; and even here we are beginning to realize that, in the words of Virginia Woolf (a writer who knew nothing about folk music, but whose words are extraordinarily applicable to our case): 'Masterpieces are not single and solitary births, they are the outcome of many years of thinking in common, of thinking by the body of the people, so that the experience of the mass is behind the single voice.'

So, in singing these songs, you may not only have great enjoyment, but you may be showing to some mute inglorious Milton the way which will lead him to musical self-expression. Sincerely, we wish you joy.

R.V.W. and A.L.L.

Introduction to the New Edition

The Penguin Book of English Folk Songs was first published in 1959, and was reprinted a number of times over the following years, most recently in 1990. This is quite an achievement for any folk song book; perhaps most particularly for one that concentrates on the English tradition. In its time it has been an inspiration and a source of material throughout the folk music revival, and now that the rights have passed to the English Folk Dance and Song Society, from whose *Journals* the songs were selected, it is especially fitting that it be made available once more in the centenary of the year in which both Cecil Sharp and Ralph Vaughan Williams began to collect songs.

The book has long been considered a classic of its kind (hence its new title) and the editors were men of considerable stature; the task of preparing a revised edition, then, is to be approached with some diffidence. The intention has been not to change (though the inevitable small errors have been silently amended) but to augment, taking into account developments since first publication. Many of the books referred to in the original notes are now very scarce and hard to obtain, so additional references to material published in the intervening years have been added. It is in the nature of books on folk song that many of these, too, are now out of print; but the scope is at least widened. The original bibliography is the only thing that has not been retained; it is replaced with a new and more comprehensive one compiled by David Atkinson.

A. L. Lloyd was both scholar and writer, and the original notes to the songs are concise, informative and interesting. Inevitably, thinking on the history or interpretation of some songs has changed over the years, or new information has become available, and one function of the supplementary notes is to take this into account. Additionally, copies of the *Journals* are no longer so easy of access as they were in the 1950s, and with this in mind, further material from them has been included; background information, for example, and verses pruned from the songs as published here. There is no intention of questioning the editors' aesthetic judgement, so these verses have not been added to the songs; singers may, however, like to have them available.

The supplements are kept separate from the original notes, and are written to fit with the existing format. Their primary function is to provide information omitted in the original book. The editors made it perfectly clear that they had collated, and amended, song texts where they felt that this was desirable; such has always been the practice when preparing folk song books designed for the singer rather than the scholar, and it should be said straight away that the results are impressive by anybody's standards. Referring to editorial intervention, Lloyd wrote: 'Where we have done this, we say so in our Notes, and we give the source of our borrowing. In very rare cases, and only where it seemed otherwise very hard to make the text fit the tune, we have ventured to cancel a few words…' [1]

While this was undoubtedly the intent, the actual case is very different. Although some alterations are fully documented, others are indicated only in passing, and many are not mentioned at all. Some texts have been extensively re-written without comment, while others have been introduced *in toto* from unspecified sources. It has been the main task of the present writer to identify these sources and, in so doing, help to fulfil the editors' stated intentions. Sometimes this has been fairly straightforward, and the material in doubt has been found in the *Journals*, often on the same page as the song to which it has been added; sometimes it has been necessary to look further afield, or to go back to the manuscripts of the original collectors. Some questions can, so far, be answered only tentatively or, indeed, not at all. A full deconstruction is in any case impossible in the present format, and would be of small interest to the average reader. For those who may wish to investigate further, signposts have been provided.

This in no way diminishes the worth of the songs as they are printed here, though it is to be hoped that the provision of more information as to how they reached their present form will enhance the reader's understanding of them. It seems likely that the bulk of editorial intervention came from Lloyd. It may be that shortage of time or space prevented him from giving all the promised details; but it should also be remembered that, where folk song was concerned, he was that rare thing, both a scholar and a practitioner of note. There were times when the boundaries between those distinct rôles became blurred. His well-known, avowed reconstructions of songs such as *Jack Orion* and *The Two Magicians* are masterpieces of their kind; as Roy Palmer has written: 'Lloyd's touch was sure, and his adaptations were invariably successful in performance.' On Lloyd as editor, however, he adds: 'It seems reasonable to suggest that he should have been more forthcoming with details of his editorial interventions.' [2]

I hope in a small way to have redressed that balance so far as this book is concerned. Although there have been times when I have roundly cursed Lloyd for his creativity and the mazes it has led me into, I have ended with, if anything, an increased admiration of his abilities. Both editors were extraordinary men, and we have a great deal to thank them for.

Malcolm Douglas
Sheffield, September 2003

[1] See page x.
[2] Roy Palmer, 'A. L. Lloyd and Industrial Song', in Ian Russell, ed., *Singer, Song and Scholar*: Sheffield 1986, p. 138.

THE EDITORS

Ralph Vaughan Williams and A. L. Lloyd were major figures in the folk music revivals of, respectively, the early and the mid twentieth century. Today, Vaughan Williams is perhaps most widely known as the prolific composer of favourite pieces such as *The Lark Ascending* and *Fantasia on a Theme by Thomas Tallis*, but there was a great deal more to him than that, as the many studies and biographies well attest. A full biography of Lloyd has yet to be published (though Dave Arthur is working on one), but his importance is not to be underestimated. These notes are intended for readers who may be relatively new to the subject.

A. L. LLOYD

Albert Lancaster (Bert) Lloyd was born in 1908 at Tooting, London. In 1924, following the deaths of his parents, he left for Australia as an assisted migrant and for the next few years worked on the sheep stations, where he seems first to have developed an interest in folk song. He also began the process of self-education that continued throughout his life. Returning to England in the early 1930s, he met the Marxist historian Leslie Morton, whose ideas were to influence the theories he would later formulate on folk song, and began to frequent the Reading Room at the British Museum; it was there that he first encountered Sharp's *English Folk Song: Some Conclusions*, and the *Journals of the Folk Song Society*. He also began to work as a journalist and translator (he had a great gift for languages). In 1937 he signed on as a labourer on a whaling factory-ship. This, and a further short stint as a merchant seaman, provided material for his first script for BBC Radio, *The Voice of the Seamen* (1938), which led to a contract during which he co-wrote the influential series *Shadow of the Swastika* in collaboration with the Russian historian Igor Vinogradoff; and, with Francis Dillon, produced the ground-breaking *Saturday Night at the Eel's Foot*; a broadcast of real traditional singers rather than the classically-trained performers who had hitherto represented folk music on the radio.

Lloyd's Marxist affiliations made him unpopular with the higher levels of the BBC hierarchy, however, and his contract was not renewed. He joined the staff of *Picture Post*, and over the next ten years produced many award-winning features, often in collaboration with photographer Bert Hardy. He enlisted in the Royal Armoured Corps in 1942, but before seeing active service was seconded to the Ministry of Information as an Anglo-Soviet liaison officer.

In 1944 he published a short but influential book, *The Singing Englishman*. This was sponsored by the Workers' Musical Association, and was intended as a radical alternative to Sharp's *English Folksong*, hitherto the only serious attempt at a detailed analysis of the subject. Lloyd approached his thesis from a Marxist perspective, arguing that folk music, appropriated by the middle classes, could and should be returned to the workers who had created it; but that this would need to be done through the urban and industrial tradition. Although the book was flawed, it was to be surpassed only by his own *Folk Song in England* (1967), a work which, though in its turn due for re-evaluation, has not been equalled.

With the escalation of Cold War paranoia, Lloyd's politics eventually cost him his job at *Picture Post* and ensured that he was blacklisted by the BBC for a good many years; he decided, therefore, to make his living as a folklorist. In 1948 he began a rapprochement with EFDSS (heavily criticised in *The Singing Englishman*) and by 1952 was a member of the editorial board of the *Journal*; in the same year the first version of his collection *Come All Ye Bold Miners: Ballads and Songs of the Coalfields* appeared. He met Ewan MacColl, and the two men were prime movers in the development of the new folk music revival, setting up early folk clubs such as 'Ballads and Blues' and 'The Singers Club'; they also established themselves as influential recording artists, producing many important works both individually and in collaboration. Lloyd became artistic director of Topic Records (the WMA label) and helped make it a force to be reckoned with.

In 1959 *The Penguin Book of English Folk Songs* was first printed, and during the 1960s Lloyd resumed writing and presenting folk music documentaries for the BBC. He made recording field-trips to Eastern Europe and published a wide range of articles and record sleeve-notes, including those for his own projects such as Topic's *The Iron Muse*. By now he was also established as a serious ethnomusicologist, teaching at foreign universities and at Goldsmith's College in London. His seminal *Folk Song in England*, an extensive re-working of the ideas first explored in *The Singing Englishman*, appeared in 1967.

His influence on younger singers continued until his death. He provided scholarship, inspiration, encouragement and material (sometimes, it must be said, extensively re-made by himself) to a great many, and remained in harness to the end; at the time of his death in 1982 he was working on a translation of Constantin Brailoiu's *Problems of Ethnomusicology*.

References:
Arthur, David, 'A. L. Lloyd: A Brief Biography', in *Classic A. L. Lloyd: Traditional Songs* (Workington:

Fellside FECD98, 1994), CD booklet, pp. 2-7.

Gregory, E. David, 'A. L. Lloyd and the English Folk Song Revival', 1934-44, *Canadian Journal for Traditional Music / Revue de musique folklorique canadienne*, 25 (1997), 14-28.

Gregory, E. David, 'Starting Over: A. L. Lloyd and the Search for a New Folk Music', 1945-49, *Canadian Journal for Traditional Music / Revue de musique folklorique canadienne*, 27 (1999/2000), 20-43.

Articles by David Arthur, Vic Gammon, Roy Palmer and Leslie Shephard in *Singer, Song and Scholar*, ed. Ian Russell (Sheffield: Sheffield Academic Press, 1986).

RALPH VAUGHAN WILLIAMS

Vaughan Williams was born in 1872 at Down Ampney in the Cotswolds. He was educated at Charterhouse, then Trinity College, Cambridge, and subsequently studied under Stanford and Parry at the Royal College of Music, and later with Bruch and Ravel in Paris. His mother was a Wedgwood, and after her husband's death she moved back to the family home at Leith Hill Place in Surrey; the song-collecting Broadwoods of Lyne were friends, and Ralph was familiar with printed folk song from a fairly early age. When he first began to formulate his ideas for a new 'English School' of music, he seems to have felt that folk song was in some ways quite as foreign to him as the fashionable French and German influences he was trying to move away from; by 1902, however, he was giving lectures on folk song – sometimes with musical illustrations from Lucy Broadwood – and was becoming increasingly convinced of its importance. It was not until late in 1903, for all that, that he encountered it directly. He was invited to a Parish Tea at Ingrave, specifically to meet some singers, and the following day (4 December) he noted twenty-two songs, seven from Charles Pottipher, a seventy year old labourer. On hearing the first, *Bushes and Briars*, he experienced an epiphany not unlike that felt by Cecil Sharp when he heard *The Seeds of Love* from John England earlier the same year.

Over the following years, he noted more than 800 songs; chiefly in the Home Counties, but with forays to the North and Midlands. Many of these were published in the *Journal of the Folk Song Society*, of which he was a member of the editorial board from 1905. As a rising composer, he was more interested in the music than in the texts, and often failed to note more than a few words, if any; although this is regrettable – a fact which he recognised in later life – he was to some extent constrained by circumstances and, often, shortage of time. Much of his collecting was done alone, though he did some work with George Butterworth in Norfolk and with Ella Leather in Herefordshire; the latter also sent him written texts and cylinder recordings for transcription. The master-singer Henry Burstow also wrote out songs for him, including *Salisbury Plain* (which he had felt unable to sing for Lucy Broadwood); in other cases songs were published with words drawn largely from broadsides. He also made field recordings on the phonograph; a few of these survive and are held at the Vaughan Williams Memorial Library.

By 1913 his collecting was more or less over, though he picked up a few songs in later years. He had already begun the synthesis of the material he had acquired. The development of an 'English School' involved not merely establishing a specifically English idiom for composition, but promoting folk song as the birthright of all, and a powerful force for national cultural regeneration. That meant producing not only 'art music' for the concert hall, but also music and song for amateurs, for schools, and for churches. He had in the past spoken scornfully of the detrimental effect on sacred music of the 1861 *Hymns Ancient and Modern*; in 1906 his *English Hymnal*, including many hymns set to traditional tunes, was published, as was the *Norfolk Rhapsody*. He set numerous folk songs for schools and for choirs, and composed many pieces in the idiom, like the perennial favourite *Linden Lea*; his collaboration with Percy Dearmer and Martin Shaw on *The Oxford Book of Carols* (1928) is still a classic of its kind.

His extensive later work is beyond the scope of these brief notes. It is sufficient to say that he is regarded as one of the great British composers, and that, while he owed an enormous debt to folk song, the movement to preserve and promulgate folk song owes, in its turn, an enormous debt to him. He served on the executive committee of EFDSS until 1947, when he became President, a position which he held until his death in August 1958. The library and archive, formerly known as the Cecil Sharp Library, was renamed as a memorial to him.

References:

Heffer, Simon, *Vaughan Williams*. London, Weidenfeld & Nicholson, 2000

Kennedy, Michael, *The Works of Ralph Vaughan Williams*. Oxford, OUP, 1964

Onderdonk, Julian, 'Vaughan Williams and the Modes', in *Folk Music Journal*, vol. 7 no. 5 (1999) 609-626

Palmer, Roy, *Folk Songs Collected by Ralph Vaughan Williams*. London, Dent, 1983 and Felinfach, Llanerch, 1999

Vaughan Williams, Ursula, *R. V. W. A Biography of Ralph Vaughan Williams*. Oxford, OUP, 1964

ACKNOWLEDGEMENTS

Malcolm Douglas is a founder member of the management teams of the South Riding Folk Network and Yorkshire Folk Arts, and administers extensive websites for both organisations.

David Atkinson is the author of *The English Traditional Ballad: Theory, Method and Practice* (2002), and a member of the editorial board of *The Folk Music Journal*.

Particular thanks are due to

Malcolm Taylor of the Vaughan Williams Memorial Library for practical guidance and advice.

David Atkinson for advice and information.

Vic Gammon for advice and help with musical issues.

Roy Palmer, whose excellent books provide much valuable information on songs included here.

Richard Coomber, Alison Macfarlane and Bonny Sartin for permission to use material from their historical and genealogical researches.

The singers and collectors of the songs in this book, and all those others like them who have kept alive, against the odds and in the face of the indifference or outright hostility of the cultural establishment, so much of the traditional culture of this country.

A NOTE ON THE PRESENTATION OF THE TUNES

This modest selection of folk songs was almost ready for the press when Dr Vaughan Williams died. A few problems remained to be solved concerning the presentation of the tunes. For the way these have been dealt with in the absence of the wise and experienced partner, the responsibility must be mine.

In continental folk song collections, where the songs are presented un-set, and only the melody-line is given, it has become customary to transpose all the tunes to a common finalis, usually G. By that means, melodies may be easier compared and analysed by those wishing to do so. Owing to the range of some of our tunes Dr Vaughan Williams and I had not found the final G always convenient. Moreover, since these songs are intended to be sung rather than merely looked at, we had not considered ourselves bound to the custom of the common finalis. However, looking over the tunes as we had prepared them, I found that the majority had, as it happened, been transcribed to end either on G or D. It seemed only commonsense to bring the few remaining melodies into line. Thus, in this selection, about half the melodies end on G, the other half on D, according to their range and modal character.

It is well known that the scales on which many of our folk tunes are based are not the same as the major and minor with which we are most familiar. Some of these scales belong to the family of what are loosely called 'Greek' modes, some are considered as gapped scales because certain steps are consistently missing, while a few show peculiar structures which the scholars have hardly begun to classify as yet. None of this need frighten the reader who has no mind for musical technicalities. Certainly it never worried the traditional singer, who could not read music – perhaps could not read at all – but could sing spontaneously in what the theorists explain as the Dorian or Mixolydian mode. [1]

Our folk song editors have found it hard to throw off the habit of hearing every tune under the influence of the conventional major-minor system, and it has been usual to give 'standard' key signatures to folk tunes, even though that might involve constantly cancelling the signature by putting a natural sign before certain tones every time they appear. Some feel this practice to be illogical (it has been compared to putting up a *No Smoking* sign in a place where tobacco is unknown). On the other hand, some will argue that the hasty eye might well misread a modal tune unless given full warning where the 'odd' notes occur.

How were we to present our tunes? In the familiar way, with a major or minor signature? Or in the newer fashion, in which one refrains from putting into the key signature sharps or flats which do not occur in the tune? For better or for worse, I have decided to adopt the latter style. Thereby, perhaps, those without formal musical education may find the songs easier to read, while those with some knowledge of musical theory may reach a better understanding of the tunes.

A.L.L.

---

[1] The fact seems to have surprised some pioneers of the folk song movement. Dr Vaughan Williams had a story of one scholar who, confronted with some notations newly taken down from a folk singer, declared: 'These must be wrong. Nobody's going to tell me that an uneducated villager sings correctly in the Dorian mode when, as often as not, even our trained musicians don't know what the Dorian is!'

SPECIMEN ACCOMPANIMENTS
by R. Vaughan Williams

SALISBURY PLAIN

BANKS OF GREEN WILLOW

THE BASKET OF EGGS

ALL THINGS ARE QUITE SILENT

Sung by Mr Ted Baines, Plummer's Plain, Lower Beeding, Sussex (R.V.W. 1904)

All things are quite silent, each mortal at rest,
When me and my love got snug in one nest,
When a bold set of ruffians they entered our cave,
And they forced my dear jewel to plough the salt wave.

I begged hard for my sailor as though I begged for life.
They'd not listen to me although a fond wife,
Saying: 'The king he wants sailors, to the sea he must go,'
And they've left me lamenting in sorrow and woe.

Through green fields and meadows we ofttimes did walk,
And sweet conversation of love we have talked,
With the birds in the woodland so sweetly did sing,
And the lovely thrushes' voices made the valleys to ring.

Although my love's gone I will not be cast down.
Who knows but my sailor may once more return?
And will make me amends for all trouble and strife,
And my true love and I might live happy for life.

AS SYLVIE WAS WALKING

Sung by Mrs Ann Aston, Moonee Ponds, Victoria, Australia (T.A. 1911)

As Syl-vie was walk-ing down by the ri-ver-side,
And look-ing so sad-ly,— and look-ing so sad-ly,— And
look-ing so sad-ly up-on its swift tide,

As Sylvie was walking down by the riverside,
As Sylvie was walking down by the riverside,
And looking so sadly, and looking so sadly,
And looking so sadly upon its swift tide.

She thought on the lover that left her in pride,
She thought on the lover that left her in pride,
On the banks of the meadow, on the banks of the meadow,
On the banks of the meadow she sat down and cried.

And as she sat weeping, a young man came by,
And as she sat weeping, a young man came by.
'What ails you, my jewel, what ails you, my jewel,
What ails you, my jewel and makes you to cry?'

'I once had a sweetheart and now I have none.
I once had a sweetheart and now I have none.
He's a-gone and he's leaved me, he's a-gone, he's deceived me,
He's a-gone and he's leaved me in sorrow to mourn.

'One night in sweet slumber, I dream that I see,
One night in sweet slumber, I dream that I see,
My own dearest true love, my own dearest true love,
My own dearest true love come smiling to me.

'But when I awoke and I found it not so,
But when I awoke and I found it not so,
Mine eyes were like fountains, mine eyes were like fountains,
Mine eyes were like fountains where the water doth flow.

'I'll spread sail of silver and I'll steer towards the sun,
I'll spread sail of silver and I'll steer towards the sun,
And my false love will weep, and my false love will weep
And my false love will weep for me after I'm gone.'

2

THE BANKS OF GREEN WILLOW

Sung by Mrs Emma Overd, Langport, Somerset (C.J.S. 1904)

Go and get your father's good will,
And get your mother's money,
And sail right o'er the ocean
Along with young Johnny.

She had not been a-sailing
Been sailing many days, O,
Before she want some woman's help
And could not get any.

Oh, fetch me a silk napkin
To tie her head up easy,
And I'll throw her overboard
Both she and her baby.

Oh, they fetched him a napkin
And bound her head so easy,
And overboard he threw his love,
Both she and her baby.

See how my love do tumble,
See how my love do taver,
See how my love do try to swim,
That makes my heart quaver.

Oh, make my love a coffin
Of the gold that shines yellow,
And she shall be buried
By the banks of green willow.

THE BANKS OF NEWFOUNDLAND

Sung by Mr John Farr, Gwithian, Cornwall (J.E.T. 1926)

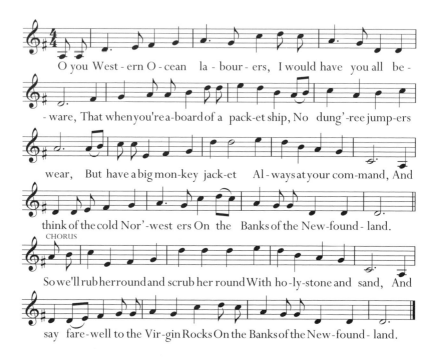

O you West-ern O-cean la-bour-ers, I would have you all be-ware, That when you're a-board of a pack-et ship, No dung'-ree jump-ers wear, But have a big mon-key jack-et Al-ways at your com-mand, And think of the cold Nor'-west ers On the Banks of the New-found-land.

CHORUS

So we'll rub her round and scrub her round With ho-ly-stone and sand, And say fare-well to the Vir-gin Rocks On the Banks of the New-found-land.

O you Western Ocean labourers,
I would have you all beware,
That when you're aboard of a packet-ship,
No dung'ree jumpers wear,
But have a big monkey jacket
Always at your command,
And think of the cold Nor'westers
On the Banks of the Newfoundland.

So we'll rub her round and scrub her round
With holystone and sand,
And say farewell to the Virgin Rocks
On the Banks of the Newfoundland.

As I lay in my bunk one night
A-dreaming all alone,
I dreamt I was in Liverpool,
'Way up in Marylebone,
With my true love beside of me,
And a jug of ale in hand,
When I woke quite broken-hearted
On the Banks of Newfoundland.

We had one Lynch from Ballinahinch,
Jimmy Murphy and Mike Moore;
It was in the winter of sixty-two,
Those sea-boys suffered sore,
For they'd pawned their clothes in Liverpool,
And sold them out of hand,
Not thinking of the cold Nor'westers
On the Banks of Newfoundland.

We had one female passenger,
Bridget Riley was her name,
To her I promised marriage
And on me she had a claim.
She tore up her flannel petticoats
To make mittens for our hands,
For she couldn't see the sea-boys freeze
On the Banks of Newfoundland.

And now we're off Sandy Hook, my boys,
And the land's all covered with snow.
The tug-boat will take our hawser
And for New York we will tow;
And when we arrive at the Black Ball dock,
The boys and girls there will stand,
We'll bid adieu to the packet-ships
And the Banks of Newfoundland.

THE BANKS OF SWEET PRIMROSES

Sung by Mrs Vaisey (late of Hertfordshire), Adwell, Oxfordshire (L.E.B. 1892)

As I walked out one mid-sum-mer's mor-ning, To view the fields and to take the air, Down by the banks of the sweet prim-ro-ses, There I__ be-held a most love-ly fair.

As I walked out one midsummer's morning,
To view the fields and to take the air,
Down by the banks of the sweet primroses,
There I beheld a most lovely fair.

I said: 'Fair maid, where can you be a-going,
And what's the occasion of all your grief?
I'll make you as happy as any lady,
If you will grant me one small relief.'

'Stand off, stand off, thou false deceiver!
You're a false deceitful man, 'tis plain.
'Tis you that is causing my poor heart to wander,
And to give me comfort is all in vain.

'Now I'll go down to some lonesome valley,
Where no man on earth there shall me find,
Where the pretty small birds do change their voices,
And every moment blows blusterous wind.'

THE BASKET OF EGGS

Sung by Mr Henry Burstow, Horsham, Sussex (R.V.W. 1903)

Down in Sand-bank fields, two sail-ors they were walk-ing, Their
pock-ets were both lined with gold, And as to-ge-ther
they were talk-ing, A fair maid there they did be-hold,
With a lit-tle bas-ket stand-ing by her,
As she sat down to take her ease. To car-ry it for her
one of them of-fered. The an-swer was: 'Sir, if you please.'

Down in Sandbank fields, two sailors they were walking,
Their pockets were both lined with gold,
And as together they were talking,
A fair maid there they did behold,
With a little basket standing by her,
As she sat down to take her ease.
To carry it for her one of them offered.
The answer was: 'Sir, if you please.'

One of these sailors took the basket.
'There's eggs in the basket, please take care;
And if by chance you should outwalk me,
At the Half-way House please leave them there.'
Behold these sailors, they did outwalk her,
The Half-way House they did pass by.
This pretty damsel she laughed at their fancy,
And on the sailors she kept her eye.

When these two sailors came unto an ale-house,
There they did call for a pint of wine,
Saying: 'Landlord, landlord, what fools in this nation!
This young maid from her eggs we've twined.
O landlord, landlord, bring us some bacon.
We have got these eggs and we'll have some dressed.'
Behold, these sailors were much mistaken,
As you shall say when you hear the rest.

'Twas then the landlord he went to the basket,
Expecting of some eggs to find.
He said: 'Young man, you're much mistaken,
Instead of eggs I've found a child.'
Then one of them sat down to weeping.
The other said: 'It's not worth while.
Here's fifty guineas I'll give to the baby,
If any woman will take the child.'

This pretty young damsel she sat by the fire,
And she had a shawl drawn over her face.
She said: 'I'll take it and kindly use it,
When first I see the money paid.'
One of the sailors threw down the money.
Great favour to the babe was shown.
'Since it is so, then let's be friendly,
For you know, this child is yours and mine.

'Don't you remember a-dancing with Nancy,
As long ago as last Easter day?'
'Oh yes, and I do, and she pleased my fancy,
So now the fiddler I have paid.'
One of the sailors went up to the basket,
And he kicked the basket over and o'er.
'Since it is so, may we all be contented,
But I'm hanged if I'll like eggs any more.'

BENJAMIN BOWMANEER

Sung by Mrs Sarah Foster, Sedburgh, Yorkshire (M.E.S. n.d.)

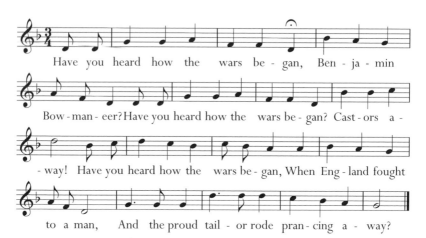

Have you heard how the wars began,
Benjamin Bowmaneer?
Have you heard how the wars began?
Castors away!
Have you heard how the wars began,
When England fought to a man,
And the proud tailor rode prancing away?

Of his shear board he made a horse,
Benjamin Bowmaneer.
Of his shear board he made a horse,
Castors away!
Of his shear board he made a horse,
All for him to ride across.
So the proud tailor rode prancing away.

Of his scissors he made bridle bits,
Benjamin Bowmaneer.
Of his scissors he made bridle bits,
Castors away!
Of his scissors he made bridle bits,
To keep the horse in its wits.
So the proud tailor rode prancing away.

As the tailor rode o'er the lea,
Benjamin Bowmaneer,
As the tailor rode o'er the lea,
Castors away!
As the tailor rode o'er the lea,
He spied a flea all on his knee.
So the proud tailor rode prancing away.

Of his needle he made a spear,
Benjamin Bowmaneer.
Of his needle he made a spear,
Castors away!
Of his needle he made a spear,
To prick that flea through its ear.
So the proud tailor rode prancing away.

Of his thimble he made a bell,
Benjamin Bowmaneer.
Of his thimble he made a bell,
Castors away!
Of his thimble he made a bell,
To ring the flea's funeral knell.
So the proud tailor rode prancing away.

'Twas thus that the wars began,
Benjamin Bowmaneer.
'Twas thus that the wars began,
Castors away!
'Twas thus that the wars began,
When England fought to a man.
And the proud tailor rode prancing away.

THE BLACKSMITH

Sung by Mrs Ellen Powell, Westhope nr Weobley, Herefordshire (R.V.W. 1909)

A blacksmith courted me, nine months and better.
He fairly won my heart, wrote me a letter.
With his hammer in his hand, he looked so clever,
And if I was with my love, I'd live for ever.

And where is my love gone, with his cheek like roses,
And his good black billycock on, decked with primroses?
I'm afraid the scorching sun will shine and burn his beauty,
And if I was with my love, I'd do my duty.

Strange news is come to town, strange news is carried,
Strange news flies up and down that my love is married.
I wish them both much joy, though they don't hear me,
And may God reward him well for slighting of me.

'What did you promise when you sat beside me?
You said you would marry me, and not deny me.'
'If I said I'd marry you, it was only for to try you,
So bring your witness, love, and I'll never deny you.'

'Oh, witness have I none save God Almighty.
And He'll reward you well for slighting of me.'
Her lips grew pale and white, it made her poor heart tremble
To think she loved one, and he proved deceitful.

THE BOLD BENJAMIN

Sung by Mr Joseph Taunton, Corscombe, Dorset (H.E.D.H. & R.F.F.H. 1907)

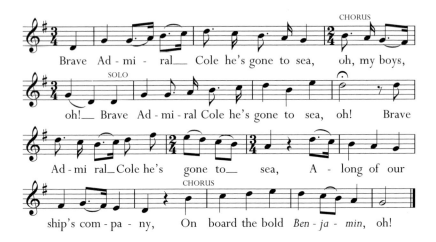

Brave Ad - mi - ral__ Cole he's gone to sea, oh, my boys,
oh!__ Brave Ad - mi - ral Cole he's gone to sea, oh! Brave
Ad - mi - ral__ Cole he's gone to__ sea, A - long of our
ship's com - pa - ny, On board the bold Ben - ja - min, oh!

Brave Admiral Cole he's gone to sea, oh, my boys, oh!
Brave Admiral Cole he's gone to sea, oh!
Brave Admiral Cole he's gone to sea,
Along of our ship's company,
On board the bold *Benjamin*, oh!

We sailed our course away for Spain, oh, my boys, oh!
We sailed our course away for Spain, oh!
We sailed our course away for Spain,
Our silver and gold for to gain,
On board the bold *Benjamin*, oh!

We sailed out five hundred men, oh, my boys, oh!
We sailed out five hundred men, oh!
We sailed out five hundred men,
And brought back but sixty one.
They were lost in bold *Benjamin*, oh!

And when we came to Blackwall, oh, my boys, oh!
And when we came to Blackwall, oh!
And when we came to Blackwall,
Our captain so loudly did call:
'Here comes the bold *Benjamin*, oh!'

Here's the mothers crying for their sons, oh, my boys, oh!
Here's the mothers crying for their sons, oh!
Here's the mothers crying for their sons,
And the widows for their husbands
That were lost in bold *Benjamin*, oh!

THE BRAMBLE BRIAR

Sung by Mrs Emma Joiner, Chiswell Green, Hertfordshire (L.E.B. & J.B. 1914)

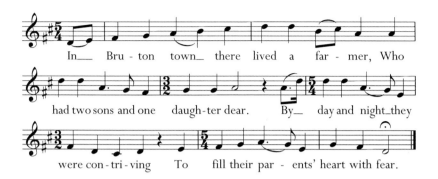

In Bruton town there lived a farmer,
Who had two sons and one daughter dear.
By day and night they were contriving
To fill their parents' heart with fear.

He told his secrets to no other,
But unto her brother this he said:
'I think our servant courts our sister.
I think they has a great mind to wed.
I'll put an end to all their courtship.
I'll send him silent to his grave.'

They asked him to go a-hunting,
Without any fear or strife,
And these two bold and wicked villains,
They took away this young man's life.

And in the ditch there was no water,
Where only bush and briars grew.
They could not hide the blood of slaughter,
So in the ditch his body they threw.

When they returned home from hunting,
She asked for her servant-man.
'I ask because I see you whisper,
So brothers tell me if you can.'

'O sister, sister, you do offend me,
Because you so examine me.
We've lost him where we've been a-hunting,
No more of him we could not see.'

As she lay dreaming on her pillow,
She thought she saw her heart's delight;
By her bed side as she lay weeping,
He was dressed all in his bloody coat.

'Don't weep for me, my dearest jewel,
Don't weep for me nor care nor pine,
For your two brothers killed me so cruel –
In such a place you may me find.'

As she rose early the very next morning,
With heavy sigh and bitter groan,
The only love that she admired,
She found in the ditch where he was thrown.

The blood upon his lips was drying.
Her tears were salt as any brine.
She sometimes kissed him, sometimes crying:
'Here lies the dearest friend of mine.'

Three days and nights she did sit by him,
And her poor heart was filled with woe,
Till cruel hunger crept upon her,
And home she was obliged to go.

When she returned to her brothers:
'Sister, what makes you look so thin?'
'Brother, don't you ask the reason,
And for his sake you shall be hung!'

11

THE BROOMFIELD HILL

Sung by Mrs Ellen Powell, Westhope nr Weobly, Herefordshire (E.M.L & R.V.W. 1910)

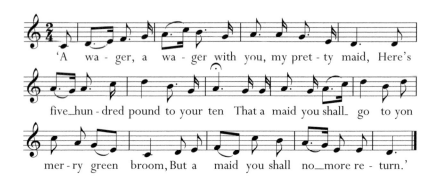

'A wa-ger, a wa-ger with you, my pret-ty maid, Here's five_hun-dred pound to your ten That a maid you shall_ go to yon mer-ry green broom, But a maid you shall no_more re-turn.'

'A wager, a wager with you, my pretty
maid,
Here's five hundred pound to your ten
That a maid you shall go to yon merry
green broom,
But a maid you shall no more return.'

'A wager, a wager with you, kind sir,
With your hundred pounds to my ten,
That a maid I will go to yon merry green
broom,
And a maid I will boldly return.'

Now when that she came to this merry
green broom,
Found her true love was fast in a sleep,
With a fine finished rose, and a new suit
of clothes,
And a bunch of green broom at his feet.

Then three times she went from the
crown of his head,
And three times from the sole of his feet,
And three times she kissed his red rosy
cheeks
As he lay fast in a sleep.

Then she took a gold ring from off her
hand,
And put that on his right thumb,
And that was to let her true love to know
That she had been there and was gone.

As soon as he had awoke from his sleep,
Found his true love had been there and
gone,
It was then he remembered upon the cost,
When he thought of the wager he'd lost.

Three times he called for his horse and his
man,
The horse he'd once bought so dear,
Saying: 'Why didn't you wake me out of
my sleep,
When my lady, my true love, was here?'

'Three times did I call to you, master,
And three times did I blow with my horn,
But out of your sleep I could not awake
Till your lady, your true love, was gone.'

'Had I been awake when my true love was here,
Of her I would had my will;
If not, the pretty birds in this merry green broom
With her blood they should all had their fill.'

THE COCK-FIGHT (THE BONNY GREY)

Sung by Mr John Collinson, Casterton, Westmorland (C.J.S. 1905)

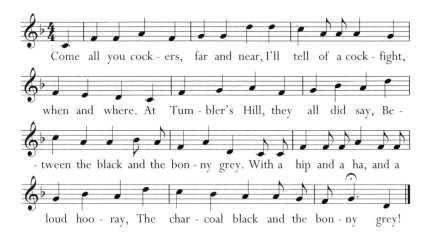

Come all you cock-ers, far and near, I'll tell of a cock-fight, when and where. At Tum-bler's Hill, they all did say, Be-tween the black and the bon-ny grey. With a hip and a ha, and a loud hoo-ray, The char-coal black and the bon-ny grey!

Come all you cockers, far and near,
I'll tell of a cock-fight, when and where.
At Tumbler's Hill, they all did say,
Between the black and the bonny grey.
    With a hip and a ha, and a loud hooray,
    The charcoal black and the bonny grey!

It's to the house to take a sup;
The cock-fight it was soon made up.
Ten guineas a side these cocks will play,
The charcoal black and the bonny grey.

Lord Derby he came swaggering down.
'I'll lay ten guineas to half a crown,
If the charcoal black he gets fair play,
He'll rip the wings off the bonny grey.'

These cocks hadn't struck past two or three blows,
When the Biggar lads cried: 'Now you'll lose.'
Which made us all both wan and pale.
We wished we'd fought for a gallon of ale.

And the cocks they at it, one, two, three,
And the charcoal black got struck in the eye.
They picked him up to see fair play,
But the black wouldn't fight with the bonny grey.

With the silver breast and the silver wing,
Six brothers of his fought before the king.
With a hip and a ha, and a loud hooray,
And away we went with our bonny grey!

THE CRUEL MOTHER

Sung by Mrs Bowring, Cerne Abbas, Dorset (H.E.D.H. & R.F.F.H. 1907)

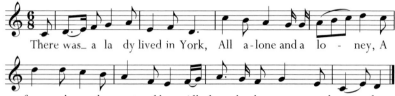

There was a lady lived in York,
  All alone and a loney,
A farmer's son he courted her
  All down by the greenwood sidey.

He courted her for seven long years.
At last she proved in child by him.

She pitched her knee against a tree,
And there she found great misery.

She pitched her back against a thorn,
And there she had her baby born.

She drew the fillet off her head.
She bound the baby's hands and legs.

She drew a knife both long and sharp.
She pierced the baby's innocent heart.

She wiped the knife upon the grass.
The more she wiped, the blood run fast.

She washed her hands all in the spring.
Thinking to turn a maid again.

As she was going to her father's hall,
She saw three babes a-playing at ball.

One dressed in silk, the other in satin,
The other star-naked as ever was born.

O, dear baby, if you was mine,
I'd dress you in silk and satin so fine.

O, dear mother, I once was thine.
You never would dress me coarse or fine.

The coldest earth it was my bed.
The green grass was my coverlet.

O, mother, mother, for your sin,
Heaven gate you shall not enter in.

There is a fire beyond hell's gate,
And there you'll burn both early and late.

THE DAUGHTER OF PEGGY, O

Sung by Mr Charles Spiller, Pitminster, Somerset (C.J.S. 1908)

There was a little man came from the
  West,
  Fol de rol de rol de rol de rigeo,
He married a wife, she was not of the best,
  She was the driggle draggle daughter of
  Peggy, O.

She wouldn't card, she wouldn't spin,
She wouldn't work all in the kitchen.

When this good man came home from
  plough,
He says: 'My dear, is the dinner ready now?'

'Oh, if your dinner you must have,
  Then get it yourself, I'm not your slave.

'For I won't brew and I won't bake,
  And I won't get my white hands black.'

This good man pulled his coat from his
  back,
  And made his stick go widgy widgy whack.

'And if you won't do what I say now,
  I'll take and yoke you to the plough.'

'Oh, I will card and I will spin,
  And I will work all in the kitchen.

'And I will bake and I will brew,
  And I will cook your dinner for you.'

DEATH AND THE LADY

Sung by Mr Baker, Maidstone, Kent (F.M.C. 1946)

As I walked out one morn in May,
The birds did sing and the lambs did play,
The birds did sing and the lambs did play,
I met an old man, I met an old man,
I met an old man by the way.

His head was bald, his beard was grey,
His coat was of a myrtle shade,
I asked him what strange countryman,
Or what strange place, or what strange
  place,
Or what strange place he did belong.

'My name is Death, cannot you see?
  Lords, dukes, and ladies bow down to me,
  And you are one of those branches three,
  And you fair maid, and you fair maid,
  And you fair maid must come with me.'

'I'll give you gold and jewels rare,
  I'll give you costly robes to wear,
  I'll give you all my wealth in store,
  If you'll let me live, if you'll let me live,
  If you'll let me live a few years more.'

'Fair lady, lay your robes aside.
  No longer glory in your pride.
  And now, sweet maid, make no delay,
  Your time is come, your time is come,
  Your time is come and you must away.'

And not long after this fair maid died.
'Write on my tomb,' the lady cried,
'Here lies a poor distressed maid,
  Whom Death now lately, whom Death
  now lately
  Whom Death now lately hath betrayed.'

15

THE DEATH OF QUEEN JANE

Sung by Mrs Marina Russell, Upwey, Dorset (H.E.D.H. & R.F.F.H. 1907)

Queen Jane lay in labour full nine days or more,
Till the women were so tirèd, they could stay no longer there. *(x2)*

'Good women, good women, good women as ye be,
Do open my right side and find my baby.'

'Oh no,' said the women, 'That never may be,
We will send for King Henry, and hear what he say.'

King Henry was sent for, King Henry did come:
'What do ail you, my lady, your eyes look so dim?'

'King Henry, King Henry, will you do one thing for me?
That's to open my right side, and find my baby.'

'Oh, no,' said King Henry, 'That's a thing I'll never do.
If I lose the flower of England, I shall lose the branch too.'

King Henry went mourning, and so did his men,
And so did the dear baby, for Queen Jane did die then.

And how deep was the mourning, how black were the bands,
How yellow, yellow were the flamboys they carried in their hands.

There was fiddling, aye, and dancing on the day the babe was born
But poor Queen Jane beloved lay cold as a stone.

THE DESERTER FROM KENT

Sung by Mr Kemp, Elstead, Surrey (W.F. 1907)

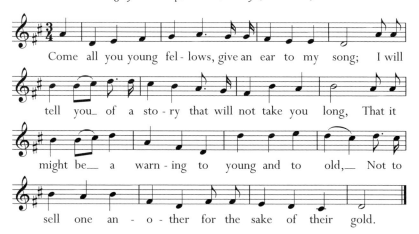

Come all you young fel-lows, give an ear to my song; I will tell you_ of a sto-ry that will not take you long, That it might be_ a warn-ing to young and to old,_ Not to sell one an-o-ther for the sake of their gold.

Come all you young fellows, give an ear to my song;
I will tell you of a story that will not take you long,
That it might be a warning to young and to old,
Not to sell one another for the sake of their gold.

It happened about a twelvemonth ago,
There was two young fellows which most of us know,
Oh, one was a deserter as plain did appear,
Came from the west of Kent up to harvesting here.

Oh, what a deceiver he met with that year!
Both sat in an alehouse a-drinking of beer.
And all in good friendship he told what he knew,
Not thinking he'd been drinking all day with the foe.

Then after a while this man went away.
He met with two soldiers that very same day.
They were after a deserter, and to him did say,
Then he swore he'd been drinking with one all the day.

Then says the soldier: 'It'll answer our plan –
One guinea we'll give you; come show us the man.'
Then 'twas 'Come along with me' the fellow did say,
And down to the alehouse went William straightway.

Then in went the soldiers without dread or fear.
'What cheer?' says the fellow, then 'Give them some beer.
What regiment are you?' 'The Ninth,' they did say.
'What regiment are you? Come tell us, we pray.'

'No regiment at all,' so bold and so gay –
'Then we'll find one for you,' the soldiers did say.
They took him and kept him in hold all that night,
Until the next morning when it was day light.

Then to Maidstone Gaol they took him straightway,
Wrote down to his regiment: 'Come fetch him away.'
They marched him through town and they marched him through city,
With his hands tied behind him, and the ladies cried pity.

And now to conclude, I will tell you my hope:
May all such informers be faced with the rope.
They would sell one another for the sake of their gain,
And no doubt they will get just reward for their pain.

THE DEVIL AND THE PLOUGHMAN

Sung by Mr Henry Burstow, Horsham, Sussex (R.V.W. 1903)

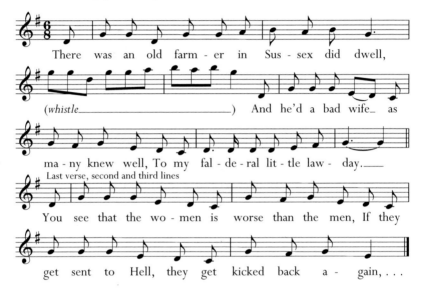

There was an old farmer in Sussex did dwell, (*whistle*)
And he'd a bad wife as many knew well,
To my fal-de-ral little law-day.

The Devil he came to the old man at plough, (*whistle*)
Saying: 'One of your family I must have now.

'Now it isn't for you nor yet for your son, (*whistle*)
But that scolding old wife as you've got at home.'

'Oh take her, oh take her with all of my heart, (*whistle*)
And I wish she and you may never more part.'

So the devil he took the old wife on his back, (*whistle*)
And lugged her along like a pedlar's pack.

He trudged along till he reached his front gate, (*whistle*)
Says: 'Here, take in an old Sussex chap's mate.'

There was thirteen imps all dancing in chains; (*whistle*)
She up with her pattens and beat out their brains.

Two more little devils jumped over the wall, (*whistle*)
Saying: 'Turn her out, father, she'll murder us all.'

So he bundled her up on his back amain, (*whistle*)
And to her old husband he took her again.

'I've been a tormentor the whole of my life, (*whistle*)
But I was never tormented till I met your wife.'

And now to conclude and make an end, (*whistle*)
You see that the women is worse than the men,
If they get sent to Hell, they get kicked back again,
To my fal-de-ral little law-day.

DROYLSDEN WAKES

Sung by Mr Allan Bates, 'heard at Droylsden, Lancashire, c.1844' (A.G.G. 1908)

It's Droylsden Wakes, an' we're comin' to town, To tell you of sommat of great renown; An' if this owd jade 'll let me begin, Aw'll show you how hard an' how fast Aw can spin,

CHORUS (slower)

So it's three-dy-well, three-dy-well, dan dum dill doe, So it's three-dy-well, three-dy-well, dan dum dill doe.

Man: It's Droylsden Wakes, an' we're comin' to town,
To tell you of sommat of great renown;
An' if this owd jade 'll let me begin,
Aw'll show you how hard an' how fast Aw can spin,
So it's threedywell, threedywell, dan dum dill doe,
So it's threedywell, threedywell, dan dum dill doe.

Woman: Thou brags of thysel, but Aw dunno' think it's true,
For Aw will uphold thee, thy faults aren't a few,
For when thou has done, an' spun very hard,
Of this Aw'm well sure, thy work is ill-marred.
So it's threedywell, etc.

19

Man: Thou saucy owd jade, thou'd best howd thy tongue,
    Or else Aw'll be thumpin' thee ere it be long,
    An' if 'at Aw do, thou'rt sure for to rue,
    For Aw can ha' mony a one's good as you.
      So it's threedywell, etc.

Woman: What is it to me who you can have?
    Aw shanno' be long ere Aw'm laid i' my grave,
    An' when 'at Aw'm dead, an' ha' done what Aw can,
    You may find one 'at'll spin as hard as Aw've done.
      So it's threedywell, etc.

THE FALSE BRIDE

Sung by Mrs Lucy White, Hambridge, Somerset (C.J.S. 1904)

Oh, when that I saw my love in the church stand,
With the ring on her finger and the glove in her hand,
I jumped in betwixt them and kissed the false bride,
Saying: 'Adieu to false loves for ever.'

Oh, when that I saw my love out the church go,
With the bridesmen and bridesmaids they made a fine show,
Then I followed after with my heart full of woe,
For I was the man that ought to had her.

Oh, when that I saw my love sat down to meat,
I sat myself by her but no thing could eat.
I thought her sweet company better than wine,
Although she was tied to some other.

Go dig me a grave both long, wide, and deep,
And strew it all over with flowers so sweet,
That I may lay down there and take my long sleep,
And that's the best way to forget her.

FARE THEE WELL, MY DEAREST DEAR

Sung by Mrs Harriet Verrall, Horsham, Sussex (R.V.W. 1904)

'Fare thee well, my dearest dear, fare thee well, adieu,
For I must go to sea for the sake of you.
Love, have a patient heart, for you must bear the smart,
Since you and I must part, my turtle dove.

'You'll have silver and bright gold, houses and land,
What more can you desire, love? Don't complain.
And jewels to your hand, and maids at your command,
But you must think of me when I am gone.'

'Your gold I'll count as dust when that you have fled,
Your absence proves me lost and strikes me dead.
And when you are from home, your servants I'll have none.
I'd rather live alone than in company.'

And so nimbly then she dressed all in man's attire,
For to go to sea was her heart's desire.
She cut her lovely hair, and no mistrust was there
That she a maiden were, all at the time.

To Venice we were bound with our hearts content,
No fear of ship being wrecked, away we went.
From London but one day, our ship was cast away,
Which caused our lives to lay in discontent.

Our ship was cast away, misfortune it did frown,
For I did swim to shore, but she was drowned.
Now she lies in the deep, in everlasting sleep,
Which causes me to weep for evermore.

GAOL SONG

Sung by Mr William Davey, Beaminster Workhouse, Dorset (H.E.D.H. & R.F.F.H. 1906)

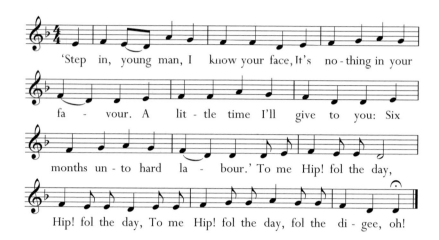

'Step in, young man, I know your face,
It's nothing in your favour.
A little time I'll give to you:
Six months unto hard labour.'
    To me Hip! fol the day, Hip! fol the day,
    To me Hip! fol the day, fol the digee, oh!

At six o'clock our turnkey comes in,
With a bunch of keys all in his hand.
'Come, come, my lads, step up and grind.
Tread the wheel till breakfast time.'
    To me Hip! etc.

At eight o'clock our skilly comes in,
Sometimes thick and sometimes thin,
But devil a word we must not say —
It's bread and water all next day.
    To me Hip! etc.

At half past eight the bell doth ring.
Into the chapel we must swing,
'Down on our bended knees to fall.
The Lord have mercy on us all.'
    To me Hip! etc.

At nine o'clock the jangle rings.
All on the trap, boys, we must spring.
'Come, come, my lads, step up in time,
The wheel to tread and the corn to grind.'
    To me Hip! etc.

Now Saturday's come, I'm sorry to say,
Sunday is our starvation day.
Our hobnail boots and tin mugs too,
They are not shined nor they will not do.
    To me Hip! etc.

Now six long months are over and past,
I will return to my bonny bonny lass,
I'll leave the turnkeys all behind,
The wheel to tread and the corn to grind.
    To me Hip! etc.

22

THE GENTLEMAN SOLDIER

Sung by Mr Thomas Coomber, Blackham, Sussex (A.G.G. 1907)

It's of a gentleman soldier, as a sentry he did stand,
He kindly saluted a fair maid by waving of his hand.
So boldly then he kissed her, and passed it as a joke.
He drilled her into the sentry-box, wrapped up in a soldier's cloak.

For the drums did go with a rap-a-tap-tap,
And the fifes did loudly play,
Saying: 'Fare you well, my Polly dear,
I must be going away.'

Oh, there they tossed and tumbled, till daylight did appear.
The soldier rose, put on his clothes, saying: 'Fare you well, my dear,
For the drums they are a-beating, and the fifes so sweetly play;
If it warn't for that, dear Polly, along with you I'd stay.'

'Now, come, you gentleman soldier, and won't you marry me?'
'Oh no, my dearest Polly, such things can never be,
For married I am already, and children I have three.
Two wives are allowed in the army, but one's too many for me!

'If anyone come a-courting you, you treat 'em to a glass.
If anyone come a-courting, you say you're a country lass.
You needn't even tell them that ever you played this joke,
That ever you went in a sentry-box, wrapped up in a soldier's cloak.'

23

'It's come, my gentleman soldier, why didn't you tell me so?
My parents will be angry when this they come to know.'
When long nine months was up and past, this poor girl she brought shame,
For she had a little militia boy, and she couldn't tell his name.

GEORDIE

Sung by Mr Charles Neville, East Coker, Somerset (C.J.S. 1908)

As I came over London Bridge
One misty morning early,
I overheard a fair pretty maid
Lamenting for her Geordie.

'Come bridle me my milk-white horse,
Come bridle me my pony,
That I may ride to London's court,
To plead for the life of Geordie.'

And when she entered in the hall,
There was lords and ladies plenty.
Down on her bended knee she fall,
To plead for the life of Geordie.

'Oh, Geordie stole no cow nor calf,
Nor sheep he never stole any,
But he stole sixteen of the king's wild deer,
And sold them in Bohenny.

'Oh, two brave children I've had by him,
And the third lies in my bosom;
And if you would spare my Geordie's life,
I'd freely part from them every one.'

The judge looked over his left shoulder,
And said: 'I'm sorry for thee.
My pretty fair maid, you come too late,
For he's condemned already.'

'Let Geordie hang in golden chains,
Such chains as never was any,
Because he came of the royal blood,
And courted a virtuous lady.

'I wish I was in yonder grove,
Where times I have been many,
With my broad sword and pistol too,
I'd fight for the life of Geordie.'

GEORGE COLLINS

Sung by Mr Henry Stansbridge, Lyndhurst, Hampshire (G.B.G. & J.F.G. 1906)

George Collins walked out one May morning
When May was all in bloom.
There he espied a fair pretty maid
A-washing her marble stone.

She whooped, she holloed, she highered her voice,
She held up her lilywhite hand.
'Come hither to me, George Collins,' she said,
'For your life shall not last you long.'

He put his foot on the broad water side,
And over the lea sprung he.
He embraced her around the middle so small,
And kissed her red rosy cheeks.

George Collins rode home to his father's own gate.
'Rise, mother, and make my bed,
And I will trouble my dear sister
For a napkin to tie round my head.

'And if I should chance to die this night,
As I suppose I shall,
Bury me under that marble stone
That's against fair Eleanor's hall.'

Fair Eleanor sat in her room so fine,
Working her silken skein.
She saw the fairest corpse a-coming
That ever the sun shone on.

She said unto her Irish maid:
'Whose corpse is this so fine?'
'This is George Collins' corpse a-coming,
That once was a true lover of thine.'

'Come put him down, my six pretty lads,
And open his coffin so fine,
That I might kiss his lilywhite lips,
For ten thousand times he has kissed mine.

'You go upstairs and fetch me the sheet
That's wove with the silver twine,
And hang that over George Collins' head.
Tomorrow it shall hang over mine.'

The news was carried to London town,
And wrote on London gate,
That six pretty maids died all of one night,
And all for George Collins' sake.

THE GOLDEN VANITY

Sung by Mr William Bolton, Southport, Lancashire (A.G.G. 1906)

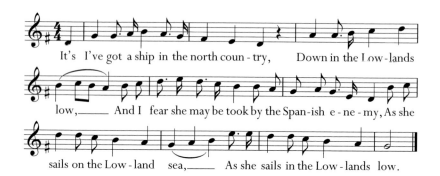

It's I've got a ship in the north coun-try, Down in the Low-lands low,_____ And I fear she may be took by the Span-ish e-ne-my, As she sails on the Low-land sea,_____ As she sails in the Low-lands low.

It's I've got a ship in the north country,
Down in the Lowlands low,
And I fear she may be took by the Spanish enemy,
As she sails on the Lowland sea,
As she sails in the Lowlands low.

And up then stepped a little cabin boy,
Down in the Lowlands low,
Saying: 'What'll you give me if I do them destroy,
And sink them in the Lowland sea,
And sink them in the Lowlands low?'

'Oh, I'll give you silver and likewise gold,
Down in the Lowlands low,
And my only daughter for to be your bride,
If you'll sink them in the Lowland sea,
If you'll sink them in the Lowlands low.'

'Oh wrap me up in my black bear skin,
Down in the Lowlands low,
And heave me overboard for to sink or to swim,
And I'll sink them in the Lowland sea,
I'll sink them in the Lowlands low.'

Now some was playing cards and the others playing dice,
Down in the Lowlands low,
And the boy had an auger, bored two holes at once,
And he sunk them in the Lowland sea,
And he sunk them in the Lowlands low.

He leaned upon his breast and he swum back again,
Down in the Lowlands low,
Saying: 'Master, take me up, for I'm sure I will be slain,
And I've sunk her in the Lowland sea,
And I've sunk her in the Lowlands low.'

'I'll not take you up,' the master he cried,
  Down in the Lowlands low,
'But I'll shoot you and kill you and send you with the tide,
  And I'll drown you in the Lowland sea,
  And I'll drown you in the Lowlands low.'

He leaned upon his breast and swum round the larboard side,
  Down in the Lowlands low,
'O messmates, take me up for I fear I will be slain,
  And I've sunk her in the Lowland sea,
  And I've sunk her in the Lowlands low.'

His messmates took him up, and on the deck he died,
  Down in the Lowlands low,
And they wrapped him up in an old cow's hide,
  And they sunk him in the Lowland sea,
  And sunk him in the Lowlands low.

THE GREEN BED

Sung by Mr Benjamin Arnold, Easton, nr Winchester (G.B.G. & H.B.G. 1906, R.V.W. 1909)

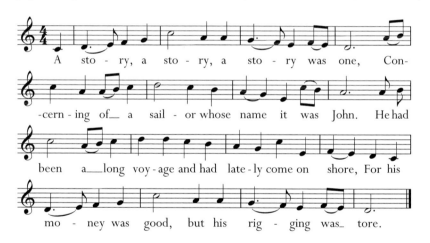

A story, a story, a story was one, Con-cern-ing of a sail-or whose name it was John. He had been a long voy-age and had late-ly come on shore, For his mo-ney was good, but his rig-ging was tore.

A story, a story, a story was one,
Concerning of a sailor whose name it was John.
He had been a long voyage and had lately come on shore,
For his money was good, but his rigging was tore.

Johnny went to an ale-house where he'd been before,
And he called for a glass of the very best beer.
'You're welcome in, young Johnny, you're welcome in,' said she,
'For last night my daughter Molly was dreaming of thee.'

'What news, my young Johnnie, what news from the sea?'
'Bad news,' says young Johnnie, 'for all's gone from me.
Our ship sprung a leak, ma'am, the voyage being crossed,
And on the wide ocean, crew and cargo was lost.

'Call down your daughter Molly and sit her on my knee.
We'll drown all our sorrows and merry we'll be.'
'My daughter Molly's busy, John, and cannot come to you,
And neither would I trust you for one pot nor two.'

Johnny being tired, he hung down his head.
He called for a candle to light him to bed.
'Our beds are all engaged, John, and will be for a week,
So now for fresh lodgings you must go and seek.'

'Oh, what is your reckoning?' the sailor he said.
'Oh what is your reckoning? for you shall be paid.'
'There's forty four shillings, John, you owe me of old.'
Then out of his pocket he drew handfuls of gold.

At the sight of this money, the landlady did rue.
'I'll have you remember all I've done for you,
For what I've just said, John, was all said in jest.
Of all of my boarders I like you the best.'

At the jingle of his money, young Molly flew downstairs.
She huddled him and cuddled him and called him her dear.
'The green bed is empty, and has been all week,
Where you and young Molly can take your sweet sleep.'

'Before I would lie in your green bed, I know,
I would rather lie out in the rain and the snow,
For if I'd no money, out of doors I'd be turned,
And it's you and your green bed deserve to be burned.'

Come all you young sailors that sails on the main,
That do get your living in cold storms of rain;
Now, when you have got it, pray lay it up in store,
For the fear that your companions should turn you out of doors.

THE GREENLAND WHALE FISHERY

Sung by Mr William Bolton, Southport, Lancashire (A.G.G. 1906)

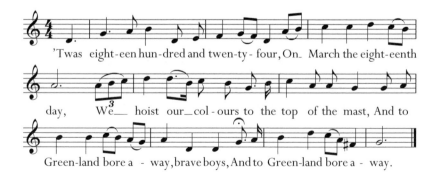

'Twas eight-een hun-dred and twen-ty-four, On March the eight-eenth day, We hoist our col-ours to the top of the mast, And to Green-land bore a-way, brave boys, And to Green-land bore a-way.

'Twas eighteen hundred and twenty four,
On March the eighteenth day,
We hoist our colours to the top of the mast,
And to Greenland bore away, brave boys,
And to Greenland bore away.

Oh, the look-out up on the mainmast stood
With a spy-glass in his hand.
'There's a whale, there's a whale, and a whale-fish,' he cried,
'And she blows at every span, brave boys,
And she blows at every span.'

The captain stood on the quarterdeck,
And the ice was in his eye.
'Overhaul, overhaul, let your jib-sheet fall,
And put your boats to sea, brave boys,
And put your boats to sea!'

Oh, the boats got down and the men aboard,
And the whale was full in view.
Resolved, resolved was each whalerman bold
To steer where the whale-fish blew, brave boys,
To steer where the whale-fish blew.

Now the harpoon struck and the lines played out,
But she gave such a flourish with her tail,
She capsized our boat and we lost five men,
And we could not catch that whale, brave boys,
And we could not catch that whale.

Oh, the losing of that sperm-whale fish
It grieved our captain sore,
But the losing of those five jolly tars,
Oh, it grieved him ten times more, brave boys,
Oh, it grieved him ten times more.*

'Up anchor now,' the captain cried,
'For the winter's star do appear,
It is time for to leave this cold country,
And for England we will steer, brave boys,
And for England we will steer.'

Oh, Greenland is a barren place,
It's a place that bears no green,
Where there's ice and snow, and the whale-fish blow,
And the daylight's seldom seen, brave boys,
And the daylight's seldom seen.

* In some more modern versions, the two sources of grief are put
  in reverse order.

THE GREY COCK OR THE LOVER'S GHOST

Sung by Mrs Cecilia Costello, Birmingham (M.S. & P.S.-S. 1951)

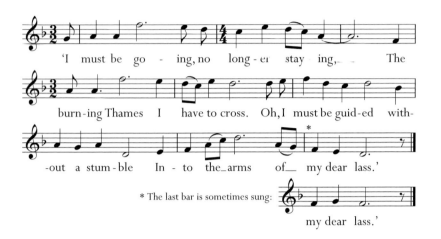

'I must be go-ing, no long-er stay-ing,— The burn-ing Thames I have to cross. Oh, I must be guid-ed with-out a stum-ble In-to the arms of my dear lass.'

* The last bar is sometimes sung:

my dear lass.'

'I must be going, no longer staying,
The burning Thames I have to cross.
Oh, I must be guided without a stumble
Into the arms of my dear lass.'

When he came to his true love's window,
He knelt down gently on a stone,
And it's through a pane he whispered slowly:
'My dear girl, are you alone?'

She rose her head from her down-soft pillow,
And snowy were her milk-white breasts,
Saying: 'Who's there, who's there at my bedroom window,
Disturbing me from my long night's rest?'

'Oh, I'm your love and don't discover,*
I pray you rise, love, and let me in,
For I am fatigued from my long night's journey.
Besides, I am wet into the skin.'

Now this young girl rose and put on her clothing.
She quickly let her own true love in.
Oh, they kissed, shook hands, and embraced together,
Till that long night was near an end.

'O Willie dear, O dearest Willie,
Where is that colour you'd some time ago?'
'O Mary dear, the clay has changed me.
I'm but the ghost of your Willie O.'

* Perhaps the phrase should be: 'but I can't uncover'
(can't reveal myself).

'Then O cock, O cock, O handsome cockerel,
I pray you not crow until it is day.
For your wings I'll make of the very first beaten gold,
And your comb I'll make of the silver grey.'

But the cock it crew, and it crew so fully.
It crew three hours before it was day.
And before it was day, my love had to go away.
Not by the light of the moon or the light of day.

Then it's 'Willie dear, O dearest Willie,
Whenever shall I see you again?'
'When the fish they fly, love, and the sea runs dry, love,
And the rocks they melt in the heat of the sun.'

I WISH, I WISH

Sung by Mrs Cecilia Costello, Birmingham (M.S. & P.S.-S.1951)

I wish, I wish, but it's all in vain,
I wish I were a maid again;
But a maid again I never shall be
Till apples grow on an orange tree.

I wish my baby it was born,
And smiling on its papa's knee,
And I to be in yon churchyard,
With long green grass growing over me.

When my apron-strings hung low,
He followed me through frost and snow,
But now my apron's to my chin,
He passes by and says nothing.

Oh grief, oh grief, I'll tell you why –
That girl has more gold than I;
More gold than I and beauty and fame,
But she will come like me again.

JACK THE JOLLY TAR

Sung by Mrs Louie Hooper, Hambridge, Somerset (C.J.S. 1904)

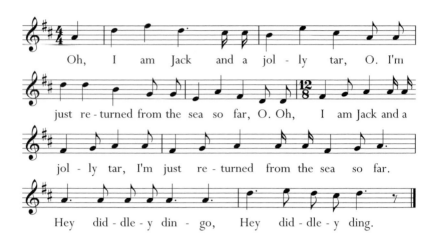

Oh, I am Jack and a jolly tar, O. I'm just re-turned from the sea so far, O. Oh, I am Jack and a jol-ly tar, I'm just re-turned from the sea so far. Hey did-dle-y din-go, Hey did-dle-y ding.

Oh, I am Jack and a jolly tar, O.
I'm just returned from the sea so far, O.
Oh, I am Jack and a jolly tar,
I'm just returned from the sea so far.
   Hey diddley dingo,
   Hey diddley ding.

As Jack was walking through London city,
He heard a squire talking to a lady.
And Jack he heard the squire say:
'Tonight with you, love, I mean to stay.

'You must tie a string all around your
   finger
With the other end hanging out the
   window,
And I'll slip by and pull the string
And you must come down and let me in.'

'Damn me,' says Jack, 'if I don't venture
For to pull that string hanging out the
   window.'
So he slipped by and he pulled the string,
And the lady came down and let him in.

The squire came by all in a passion,
Saying: 'Curse the women throughout the
   nation!
For here I am, no string I've found,
Behold my hopes all gone aground!'

Early in the morning, the sun was gleaming,
The lady woke up and started screaming,
For there's old Jack in his tarry shirt,
And behold his face all streaked with dirt.

'Oh what is this, you tarry sailor?
Have you broken in for to steal my
   treasure?'
'Oh no,' says Jack, 'I just pulled the string,
And you came down, ma'am, and let me in.'

'Oh,' then says Jack, 'won't you please forgive
   me?
I'll steal away so no-one shall see me.'
'Oh no,' says she, 'don't stray too far,
For I never will part from my jolly Jack Tar.'
   Hey diddley dingo,
   Hey diddley ding.

JOHN BARLEYCORN

Sung by Shadrack 'Shepherd' Hayden, Bampton, Oxfordshire (C.J.S. 1909)

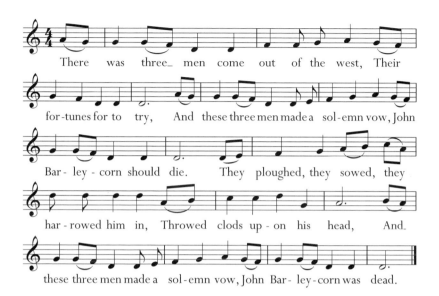

There was three men came out of the west,
Their fortunes for to try,
And these three men made a solemn vow,
John Barleycorn should die.
They ploughed, they sowed, they harrowed him in,
Throwed clods upon his head,
And these three men made a solemn vow,
John Barleycorn was dead.

Then they let him lie for a very long time
Till the rain from heaven did fall,
Then little Sir John sprung up his head,
And soon amazed them all.
They let him stand till midsummer
Till he looked both pale and wan,
And little Sir John he growed a long beard
And so became a man.

They hired men with the scythes so sharp
To cut him off at the knee,
They rolled him and tied him by the waist,
And served him most barbarously.
They hired men with the sharp pitchforks
Who pricked him to the heart,
And the loader he served him worse than that,
For he bound him to the cart.

They wheeled him round and round the field
Till they came unto a barn,
And there they made a solemn mow
Of poor John Barleycorn.
They hired men with the crab-tree sticks
To cut him skin from bone,
And the miller he served him worse than that,
For he ground him between two stones.

Here's little Sir John in a nut-brown bowl,
And brandy in a glass;
And little Sir John in the nut-brown bowl
Proved the stronger man at last.
And the huntsman he can't hunt the fox,
Nor so loudly blow his horn,
And the tinker he can't mend kettles or pots
Without a little of Barleycorn.

LISBON

Sung by Mrs Elizabeth Lock, Muchelney Ham, Somerset (C.J.S. 1904)

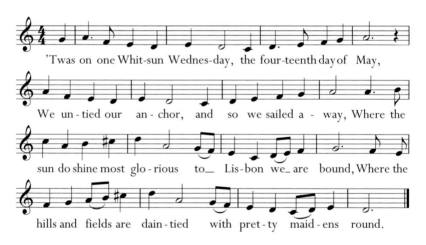

'Twas on one Whit-sun Wednes-day, the four-teen day of May,
We un-tied our an-chor, and so we sailed a-way, Where the
sun do shine most glo-rious to_ Lis-bon we_ are bound, Where the
hills and fields are dain-tied with pret-ty maid-ens round.

'Twas on one Whitsun Wednesday, the fourteenth day of May,
We untied our anchor, and so we sailed away,
Where the sun do shine most glorious, to Lisbon we are bound,
Where the hills and fields are daintied with pretty maidens round.

I wrote a letter to Nancy, for she to understand
That I was going to leave her, unto some foreign land.
She said: 'My dearest William, those words will break my heart,
Oh, let us married be tonight before that you do start.

'For ten long weeks and better, love, I've been with child by thee,
So stay at home, dear William; be kind and marry me.'
'Our captain has commanded us and I shall have to go.
For the Queen's in want of men, my love, I dare not answer No.'

'Oh, I'll cut off my yellow hair, men's clothing I'll put on,
 And I will go along with you and be your waiting man,
 And when it is your watch on deck, your duty I will do.
 I'd face the field of battle, love, so I could be with you.'

'Your pretty little fingers, they are both long and small.
 Your waist it is too slender to face the cannon-ball.
 For the cannons loud do rattle and the blazing bullets fly,
 And the silver trumpets they do sound to drown the dismal cry.

'If I should meet a pretty girl that's proper tall and gay,
 If I should take a fancy to her, Polly, what would you say?
 Would you not be offended?' 'Oh no, my lover true,
 I'd stand aside, sweet William, while she does pleasure you.

'Pray do not talk of danger, for love is my desire,
 To see you in the battle and with you spend my time;
 And I will travel through France and Spain all for to be your bride,
 And within the field of battle I will lay down by your side.'

LONG LANKIN

Sung by Sister Emma, Clewer, Buckinghamshire (C.J.S. 1909)

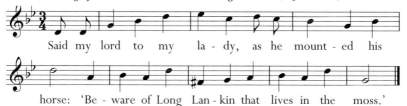

Said my lord to my la-dy, as he mount-ed his horse: 'Be-ware of Long Lan-kin that lives in the moss.'

Said my lord to my lady, as he mounted his horse:
'Beware of Long Lankin that lives in the moss.'

Said my lord to my lady, as he rode away:
'Beware of Long Lankin that lives in the hay.'

'Let the doors be all bolted and the windows all pinned,
And leave not a hole for a mouse to creep in.'

So he kissed his fair lady and he rode away,
And he was in fair London before the break of day.

The doors were all bolted and the windows all pinned,
Except one little window where Long Lankin crept in.

'Where's the lord of this house?' said Long Lankin,
'He's away in fair London.' said the false nurse to him.

'Where's the little heir of this house?' said Long Lankin.
'He's asleep in his cradle,' said the false nurse to him.

'We'll prick him, we'll prick him all over with a pin,
And that'll make my lady to come down to him.'

So he pricked him, he pricked him all over with a pin,
And the nurse held the basin for the blood to flow in.

'O nurse, how you slumber. O nurse, how you sleep.
You leave my little son Johnson to cry and to weep.

'O nurse, how you slumber, O nurse how you snore.
You leave my little son Johnson to cry and to roar.'

'I've tried him with an apple, I've tried him with a pear.
Come down, my fair lady, and rock him in your chair.

'I've tried him with milk and I've tried him with pap.
Come down, my fair lady, and rock him in your lap.'

'How durst I go down in the dead of the night
Where there's no fire a-kindled and no candle alight?'

'You have three silver mantles as bright as the sun.
Come down, my fair lady, all by the light of one.'

My lady came down, she was thinking no harm.
Long Lankin stood ready to catch her in his arm.

Here's blood in the kitchen. Here's blood in the hall.
Here's blood in the parlour where my lady did fall.

Her maiden looked out from the turret so high,
And she saw her master from London riding by.

'O master, O master, don't lay the blame on me.
'Twas the false nurse and Lankin that killed your lady.'

Long Lankin was hung on a gibbet so high
And the false nurse was burnt in a fire close by.

LORD THOMAS AND FAIR ELEANOR

Sung by Mrs Anna Pond, Shepton Beauchamp, Somerset (C.J.S. 1904)

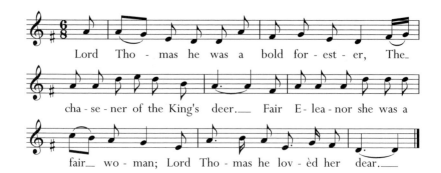

Lord Tho - mas he was a bold for - est - er, The cha - se - ner of the King's deer. Fair E - lea - nor she was a fair wo - man; Lord Tho - mas he lov - èd her dear.

Lord Thomas he was a bold forester,
The chasener of the King's deer.
Fair Eleanor she was a fair woman;
Lord Thomas he lovèd her dear.

'Oh riddle, Oh riddle, dear mother,' he said,
'Oh riddle it both as one,
Whether I shall marry fair Ellen or not,
And leave the brown girl alone?'

'The brown girl she've a-got houses and land,
Fair Ellen she've a-got none,
Therefore I charge thee to my blessing
To bring the brown girl home.'

Lord Thomas he went to fair Eleanor's tower.
He knocked so loud on the ring.
There was none so ready as fair Eleanor's self
To let Lord Thomas in.

'What news, what news, Lord Thomas?' she said,
'What news have you brought to me?'
'I've come to invite thee to my wedding
Beneath the sycamore tree.'

'O God forbid, Lord Thomas,' she said,
'That any such thing should be done.
I thought to have been the bride myself,
And you to have been the groom.'

'Oh riddle, Oh riddle, dear mother,' she said,
'Oh riddle it both as one,
Whether I go to Lord Thomas's wedding,
Or better I stay at home?'

'There's a hundred of thy friends, dear child,
A hundred of thy foes,
Therefore I beg thee with all my blessing
To Lord Thomas's wedding don't go.'

But she dressed herself in her best attire,
Her merry men all in green,
And every town that she went through,
They thought she was some queen.

Lord Thomas he took her by the hand,
He led her through the hall,
And he sat her down in the noblest chair
Among the ladies all.

'Is this your bride, Lord Thomas?' she says.
'I'm sure she looks wonderful brown,
When you used to have the fairest young lady
That ever the sun shone on.'

'Despise her not,' Lord Thomas he said,
'Despise her not unto me.
For more do I love your little finger
Than all her whole body.'

This brown girl she had a little pen-knife
Which was both long and sharp.
And betwixt the long ribs and the short
She pricked fair Eleanor's heart.

'Oh, what is the matter?' Lord Thomas he said.
'Oh, can you not very well see?
Can you not see my own heart's blood
Come trickling down my knee?'

Lord Thomas's sword is hung by his side,
As he walked up and down the hall,
And he took off the brown girl's head from
    her shoulders,
And he flung it against the wall.

He put the handle to the ground,
The sword into his heart.
No sooner did three lovers meet,
No sooner did they part.

Lord Thomas was buried in the church,
Fair Eleanor in the choir,
And out of her bosom there grew a red rose,
And out of Lord Thomas a briar.

And it grew till it reached the church steeple
    top,
Where it could grow no higher,
And there it entwined like a true lover's knot
For all true loves to admire.

LOVELY JOAN

Sung by Mr Christopher Jay, Acle, Norfolk (R.V.W. 1908)

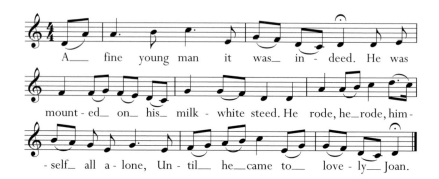

A fine young man it was indeed. He was mount-ed on his milk-white steed. He rode, he rode, him-self all a-lone, Un-til he came to love-ly Joan.

A fine young man it was indeed.
He was mounted on his milk-white steed.
He rode, he rode, himself all alone,
Until he came to lovely Joan.

'Good morning to you, pretty maid.'
And 'Twice good morning, sir', she said.
He gave her a wink, she rolled her eye.
Says he to himself: 'I'll be there by and by.'

'Oh don't you think these pooks of hay
A pretty place for us to play?
So come with me like a sweet young thing,
And I'll give you my golden ring.'

Then he pulled off his ring of gold.
'My pretty little miss, do this behold.
I'd freely give it for your maidenhead.'
And her cheeks they blushed like the roses red

'Give me that ring into my hand,
And I will neither stay nor stand,
For this would do more good to me
Than twenty maidenheads,' said she.

And as he made for the pooks of hay,
She leaped on his horse and tore away.
He called, he called, but it was all in vain;
Young Joan she never looked back again.

She didn't think herself quite safe,
No, not till she came to her true love's gate.
She's robbed him of his horse and ring,
And left him to rage in the meadows green.

LUCY WAN

Sung by Mrs Charlotte Dann, Cottenham, Cambridgeshire (E.B. &W.P.M. c.1904)

Fair Lu-cy she sits at her fa-ther's door, A weep-ing and mak-ing moan, And by there came her bro-ther dear: 'What ails thee, Lu-cy Wan?'

Fair Lucy she sits at her father's door,
A-weeping and making moan,
And by there came her brother dear:
'What ails thee, Lucy Wan?'

'I ail, and I ail, dear brother,' she said,
'I'll tell you the reason why;
There is a child between my two sides,
Between you, dear Billy, and I.'

And he has drawn his good broad sword,
That hung down by his knee,
And he has cutted off Lucy Wan's head,
And her fair body in three.

'Oh, I have cutted off my greyhound's head,
And I pray you pardon me.'
'Oh, this is not the blood of our greyhound,
But the blood of our Lucy.'

'Oh, what shall you do when your father comes to know?
My son, pray tell unto me.'
'I shall dress myself in a new suit of blue
And sail to some far country.'

'Oh, what will you do with your houses and your lands?
My son, pray tell unto me?'
'Oh, I shall leave them all to my children so small,
By one, by two, by three.'

'Oh, when shall you turn to your own wife again?
My son, pray tell unto me.'
'When the sun and the moon rise over yonder hill,
And I hope that may never, never be.'

THE MANCHESTER 'ANGEL'

Sung by Mr Sam Gregory, Beaminster, Dorset (H.E.D.H. & R.F.F.H. 1906)

It's coming down to Manchester to gain my liberty,
I met a pretty young doxy and she seemèd full of glee.
Yes, I met a pretty young doxy, the prettiest ever I see.
At the Angel Inn in Manchester, there is the girl for me.

Then early next morning, just at the break of day,
I went to my love's bedside, my morning vows to pay.
I hugged her, I cuddled her, I bade her to lie warm;
And she said: 'My jolly soldier, do you mean me any harm?'

'To mean you any harm, my love, is a thing that I would scorn.
If I stopped along with you all night, I'd marry you in the morn.
Before my lawful officer, my vows I will fulfil.'
Then she said, 'My jolly soldier, you may lie as long as you will.'

Our rout came on the Thursday, on the Monday we marched away.
The drums and fifes and bugles so sweetly did play.
Some hearts they were merry, but mine was full of woe.
She says: 'May I go along with you?' 'Oh no, my love, oh no.'

'If you should stand on sentry go, on a cold and bitter day,
Your colours they would go, love, and your beauty would decay.
If I saw you handle a musket, love, it would fill my heart with woe
So stay at home, dear Nancy.' But still she answered: 'No.

'I'll go down to your officer, and I'll buy your discharge,
Ten guineas I'll surrender if they'll set you at large.
And if that will not do, my love, along with you I'll go,
So will you take me with you now?' And still I answered: 'No.'

'I'll go down in some nunnery and there I'll end my life.
I'll never have no lover now, nor yet become a wife.
But constant and true-hearted, love, for ever I'll remain,
And I never will get married till my soldier comes again!'

THE MAN OF BURNINGHAM TOWN

Sung by Mr George Locke, Rollesby, Norfolk (R.V.W. 1908)

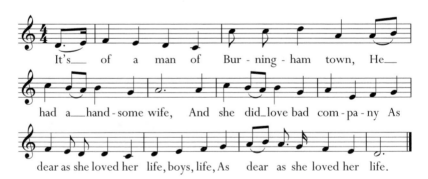

It's of a man of Burningham town,
He had a handsome wife,
And she did love bad company
As dear as she loved her life, boys, life,
As dear as she loved her life.

Now this poor man would go to sea,
His living for to get.
Where he made one penny, she spent two.
It was all for want of wit, boys, wit,
It was all for want of wit.

Now this poor man came home from sea,
It being all late in the night,
He enquired after his own dear wife,
His joy and his heart's delight, boys, light,
His joy and his heart's delight.

Oh, the servant girl she made this reply,
With a voice so wonderful strong:
'She's gone unto the neighbour's house,
And I think she may tarry there long, boys, long,
And I think she may tarry there long.

'Oh, shall I go and fetch her home?'
The poor man begun for to think.
'Oh no,' says he, 'I'll go there myself,
For I think I could do with a drink, boys, drink,
For I think I could do with a drink.'

Now, as he was a-going along of the road,
He heard such a wonderful noise.
And who should it be but his own dear wife,
Along with the Burningham boys, brave boys,
Along with the Burningham boys.

He heard her say: 'Fetch us another full glass,
And I will sit down on your knee,
And we'll fairly well make this old tavern to roar
While our husbands are on the sea, boys, sea,
While our husbands are on the sea.'

This poor man he stood at the door in a maze;
His heart it was very nigh broke,
Then he went back home and he sent out the maid,
While he prepared a rope, boys, rope,
While he prepared a rope.

Then she came a-jumping and skipping in,
Gave him such a joyful kiss,
Saying: 'You're welcome home, my kind husband so dear.
Long time you have been missed, boys, missed,
Long time you have been missed.'

He beat her once, he beat her twice,
Till she was wonderful sore;
And she cries out: 'Oh, my husband dear,
I'll never do the likes any more, boys, more,
I'll never do the likes any more.'

So come all you girls of Burningham town,
A warning take by me;
And don't you spend your money to waste,
While your husband is on the sea, the sea,
While your husband is on the sea.

For if you do they'll make you rue,
And curse the hour you were born,
For the cuckolding of your husband dear,
They'll make you wear the horn, boys, horn,
They'll make you wear the horn.

THE MERMAID

Sung by Mr James Herridge, Twyford, Hampshire (E.T.S. 1906)

One night as I lay on my bed,
I lay so fast asleep,
When the thought of my true love came running to my head,
And poor sailors that sail on the deep.

As I sailed out one day, one day,
And being not far from land,
And there I spied a mermaid a-sitting on a rock,
With a comb and a glass in her hand.

The song she sang, she sang so sweet,
But no answer at all could us make,
Till at last our gallant ship, she tooked round about,
Which made all our poor hearts to ache.

Then up stepped the helmsman of our ship,
In his hand a lead and line,
All for to sound the seas, my boys, that is so wide and deep,
But no hard rock or sand could he find.

Then up stepped the captain of our ship,
And a well-speaking man is he.
He says: 'I have a wife, my boys, in fair Plymouth town,
But this night and a widow she will be.'

Then up stepped the bosun of our ship,
And a well-spoken man was he.
He says: 'I have two sons, my boys, in fair Bristol town,
And orphans I fear they will be.'

And then up stepped the little cabin boy,
And a pretty boy was he.
He says: 'Oh, I grieve for my own mother dear,
Whom I shall nevermore see.

'Last night, when the moon shined bright,
  My mother had sons five,
  But now she may look in the salt salt seas
  And find but one alive.'

Call a boat, call a boat, my fair Plymouth boys,
  Don't you hear how the trumpets sound?
  For the want of a long-boat in the ocean we were lost,
  And the most of our merry men drowned.

MOTHER, MOTHER, MAKE MY BED

Sung by Mrs Agnes Ford, Blackham, Sussex (A.G.G. 1906)

'Mo-ther, mo-ther, make my bed, And wrap me in a— milk-white sheet, And wrap me— in— a— cloak of gold, And see whe-ther I can sleep.'

'Mother, mother, make my bed,
  And wrap me in a milk-white sheet,
  And wrap me in a cloak of gold,
  And see whether I can sleep.

'And send me the two bailies,
  Likewise my sister's son,
  That they may fetch me my own true love,
  Or I shall die before ever he can come.'

The first three miles they walked,
  The next three miles they ran,
  Until they came to the high water side,
  And laid on their breast and swam.

They swam till they came to the high castle
  Where my lord he was sitting at meat:
'If you did but know what news I brought,
  Not one mouthful more would you eat.'

'What news, what news have you brought me?
  Is my castle burnt down?'
'Oh no, your true love is very, very ill,
  And she'll die before ever you can come.'

'Saddle me my milk-white horse,
  And bridle him so neat,
  That I may kiss of her lily lips
  That are to me so sweet.'

They saddled him his milk-white steed
  At twelve o'clock at night.
  He rode, he rode till he met six young men
  With a corpse all dressed in white.

'Come set her down, come set her down,
  Come set her down by me,
  That I may kiss of her lily, lily lips,
  Before she is taken away.'

My lady, she died on the Saturday night
  Before the sun went down.
  My lord he died on the Sunday following
  Before evening prayers began.

My lady she was buried in the high castle
  My lord was buried in the choir;
  Out of my lady grew a red rose,
  And out of my lord a sweet briar.

This rose and the briar they grew up together,
  Till they could grow no higher,
  They met at the top in a true lover's knot,
  And the rose it clung round the sweet briar.

THE NEW YORK TRADER

Sung by Mr Ted Goffin, Catfield, Norfolk (E.J.M. 1921)

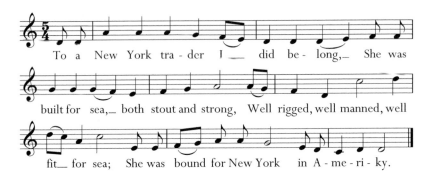

To a New York tra-der I __ did be-long, __ She was built for sea, __ both stout and strong, Well rigged, well manned, well fit __ for sea; She was bound for New York in A-me-ri-ky.

To a New York trader I did belong,
She was built for sea, both stout and strong,
Well rigged, well manned, well fit for sea;
She was bound for New York in Ameriky.

Our cruel captain, as we did find,
Left half of our provisions behind.
Our cruel captain, as we understand,
Meant to starve us all before we made the
    land.

At length our hunger grew very great.
We had but little on board to eat,
And we were in necessity,
All by our captain's cruelty.

Our captain in his cabin lay.
A voice came to him and thus did say:
'Prepare yourself and ship's company,
For tomorrow night you shall lay with me.'

Our captain woke in a terrible fright,
It being the first watch of the night,
Aloud for his bo'sun he did call,
And to him related the secret all.

'Bo'sun,' said he, 'it grieves my heart
To think I have acted a villain's part,
To take what was not my lawful due,
To starve the passengers and the ship's crew.

'There is one thing more I have to tell –
When I in Waterford town did dwell,
I killed my master, a merchant there,
All for the sake of his lady fair.

'I killed my wife and children three,
All through that cursed jealousy,
And on my servant I laid the blame,
And hanged he was all for the same.'

'Captain,' said he, 'if that be so,
Pray let none of your ship's crew know,
But keep your secret within your breast,
And pray to God to give you rest.'

Early next morning a storm did rise,
Which our seamen did much surprise;
The sea was over us, both fore and aft,
Till scarce a man on deck was left.

Then the bo'sun he did declare
That our captain was a murderer.
It so enraged the whole ship's crew
They overboard their captain threw.

When this was done a calm was there,
Our good little ship homeward did steer,
The wind abated and calmed the sea,
And we sailed safe to Ameriky.

And when we came to anchor there,
Our good little ship for to repair,
The people wondered much to see
What a poor distressed shipwrecked crew were we.

O SHEPHERD, O SHEPHERD

Sung by Mrs Davis, Dorchester, Dorset (H.E.D.H. & R.F.F.II. 1906)

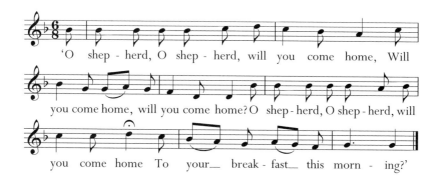

'O shep-herd, O shep-herd, will you come home, Will you come home, will you come home? O shep-herd, O shep-herd, will you come home To your_ break-fast_ this morn - ing?'

'O shepherd, O shepherd, will you come home,
Will you come home, will you come home?
O shepherd, O shepherd, will you come home
To your breakfast this morning?'

'What have you got for my breakfast,
For my breakfast, for my breakfast?
What have you got for my breakfast
If I do come home this morning?'

'Bacon and beans a bellyful,
A bellyful, a bellyful.
Bacon and beans, a bellyful
If you do come home this morning.'

'My sheep they are all in the wilderness,
The wilderness, the wilderness.
My sheep they are all in the wilderness
So I cannot come home this morning.'

'O shepherd, O shepherd, will you come home,
Will you come home, will you come home?
O shepherd, O shepherd, will you come home
To your dinner this morning?'

'What have you got for my dinner,
For my dinner, for my dinner?
What have you got for my dinner
If I do come home this morning?'

'Pudding and beef a bellyful,
A bellyful, a bellyful.
Pudding and beef a bellyful
If you do come home this morning.'

'My sheep they are all in the wilderness,
The wilderness, the wilderness.
My sheep they are all in the wilderness,
So I cannot come home this morning.'

'O shepherd, O shepherd, will you come home,
Will you come home, will you come home?
O shepherd, O shepherd, will you come home
To your supper tonight?'

'What have you got for my supper,
For my supper, for my supper?
What have you got for my supper
If I do come home tonight?'

'Bread and cheese a bellyful,
A bellyful, a bellyful.
Bread and cheese a bellyful
If you do come home tonight.'

'My sheep they are all in the wilderness,
The wilderness, the wilderness.
My sheep they are all in the wilderness,
So I cannot come home tonight.'

'O shepherd, O shepherd, will you come home,
Will you come home, will you come home?
O shepherd, O shepherd, will you come home
To your lodging tonight?'

'What have you got for my lodging,
For my lodging, for my lodging?
What have you got for my lodging
If I do come home tonight?'

'A clean pair of sheets and a pretty lass,
A pretty lass, a pretty lass.
A clean pair of sheets and a pretty lass,
If you do come home tonight.'

'Oh, I'll drive my sheep out of the wilderness,
The wilderness, the wilderness.
I'll drive my sheep out of the wilderness,
And I will come home tonight!'

The Old Man from Lee

Sung by unnamed singer, Coggeshall, Essex (G.E.McC. n.d.)

There was an old man came o'er from Lee,
Eh, but I'll not have him.
There was an old man came o'er from Lee,
A-courting me, a-courting me,
  With his old grey beard,
  With his old grey beard
Just newly shaven.

My mother she told me to get him some pie.
Eh, but I'll not have him.
My mother she told me to get him some pie,
  I got him some pie and he put the crust by,
    With his old grey beard, etc.

My mother she told me to hand him a stool.
Eh, but I'll not have him.
My mother she told me to hand him a stool.
I hand him a stool, he sat down like a fool,
  With his old grey beard, etc.

My mother she told me to give him some wine,
Eh, but I'll not have him.
My mother she told me to give him some wine.
I gave him some wine and he drank like a swine,
  With his old grey beard, etc.

My mother she told me to take him to church.
Eh, but I'll not have him.
My mother she told me to take him to church.
I took him to church but left him in the lurch,
  With his old grey beard, etc.

My mother she told me to take him to bed.
Eh, but I'll not have him.
My mother she told me to take him to bed.
I took him to bed, and he asked me to wed,
  With his old grey beard, etc.

ON MONDAY MORNING

Sung by Mr W. Alexander, Cliddesdon, Hampshire (G.B.G. & C.G. n.d., R.V.W. 1909)

On Monday morning I married a wife,
Thinking to live and a sober life,
But as she turned out, I'd better been dead,
The remarkable day that I was wed,
To me rite fol-lol-liddle-lol-le-day.

On Monday morning I married a wife,
Thinking to live and a sober life,
But as she turned out, I'd better been dead,
The remarkable day that I was wed,
To me rite fol-lol-liddle-lol-le-day.

On Tuesday morning I goes to the wood,
I cut a stick both fine and good,
The finest stick that ever you did see,
I cut him out of a holly holly tree,
To me rite fol-lol-liddle-lol-le-day.

On Wednesday morning then home goes I,
Thinking a battle I must try.
I beat him about her back and her wig,
Until I'd a-broke me holly, holly twig,
To me rite fol-lol-liddle-lol-le-day.

On Thursday morning my poor wife,
She was sick and like to die,
If she isn't better tomorrow, you see,
The devil may have her for all of me,
To me rite fol-lol-liddle-lol-le-day.

On Friday morning the sun did shine,
And I walked out in the midst of my prime,
Oh, the devil he come in, in the midst of the game,
And he took her away, both blind and lame,
To me rite fol-lol-liddle-lol-le-day.

On Saturday morning it's five days past,
My poor wife is dead at last.
The big bell shall ring and the little one shall toll,
And I'll go home like a jolly old soul,
To my rite fol-lol-liddle-lol-le-day.

On Sunday morning I dined without.
I had ne'er a wife to scold me about.
Here's good luck to my pipe, my bottle, and my friend,
And here's good luck to a week's work's end,
To my rite fol-lol-liddle-lol-le-day.

ONE NIGHT AS I LAY ON MY BED

Sung by Mrs Marina Russell, Upwey, Dorset (H.E.D.H. & R.F.F.H. 1907)

One night as I lay on my bed, I dreamed about a pretty maid. I was so distressed, I could take no rest; Love did torment me so. So away to my true love I did go.

One night as I lay on my bed,
I dreamed about a pretty maid.
I was so distressed, I could take no rest;
Love did torment me so.
So away to my true love I did go.

But when I came to my love's window,
I boldly called her by her name,
Saying: 'It was for your sake I'm come
   here so late,
Through this bitter frost and snow.
So it's open the window, my love, do.'

'My mum and dad they are both awake,
And they will sure for to hear us speak.
There'll be no excuse then but sore abuse,
Many a bitter word and blow.
So begone from my window, my love, do.'

'Your mum and dad they are both asleep,
And they are sure not to hear us speak,
For they're sleeping sound on their bed of
   down,
And they draw their breath so low.
So open the window, my love, do.'

My love arose and she opened the door,
And just like an angel she stood on the floor.
Her eyes shone bright like the stars at night,
And no diamonds could shine so.
So in with my true love I did go.

THE OUTLANDISH KNIGHT

Sung by Mr Hilton, South Walsham, Norfolk (R. V. W. 1908)

'An out-land-ish knight from the north land came, And he came woo-ing of me; And he told me he'd take me to that north-ern land, And there he would mar-ry me.'

'An outlandish knight from the north land came,
    And he came wooing of me;
    And he told me he'd take me to that northern land,
    And there he would marry me.'

'Well, go and get me some of your father's gold,
    And some of your mother's fee,
    And two of the very best stable steeds,
    Where there stand thirty and three.'

She borrowed some of her father's gold,
And some of her mother's fee,
And away they did go to the stable door,
Where horses stood thirty and three.

She mounted on her lilywhite horse,
And he upon the grey,
And away they did ride to the fair river side,
Three hours before it was day.

He says: 'Unlight, my little Polly,
Unlight, unlight,' cries he,
'For six pretty maids I've drowned here
   before,
And the seventh thou art to be.

'Pull off, pull off your silken gown,
    And deliver it unto me,
For I think it's too fine and much too gay
    To rot in the salt water sea.'

She said: 'Go get a sickle to crop the thistle
That grows beside the brim,
That it may not mingle with my curly locks,
Nor harm my lilywhite skin.'

So he got a sickle to crop the thistle,
That grew beside the brim,
She catched him around the middle so small,
And tumbled him into the stream.

'Lie there, lie there, you false-hearted man,
    Lie there instead of me,
For six pretty maidens thou has drowned here before,
    And the seventh has drowned thee.'

Then she mounted on her lilywhite horse,
    And she did ride away,
And she arrived at her father's stable door
    Three hours before it was day.

Now the parrot being in the window so high,
A-hearing the lady, he did say:
'I'm afraid that some ruffian have led you astray,
That you've tarried so long away.'

Now the master being in the bedroom so high,
A-hearing the parrot he did say:
'What's the matter with you, my pretty Polly,
You're prattling so long before day?'

'Don't prittle, don't prattle, my pretty Polly,
Nor tell no tales of me,
And your cage shall be of the glittering gold,
And your perch of the best ivory.'

'There come an old cat on top of my cage,
To take my sweet life away.
I was just calling on my young mistress
To drive that old puss away.'

T'OWD YOWE WI' ONE HORN

Sung by Mr Dean Robinson, Scawby Brook, Lincolnshire (P.G. 1905)

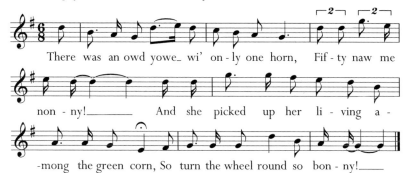

There was an owd yowe_ wi' on-ly one horn, Fif-ty naw me non-ny!_____ And she picked up her li-ving a--mong the green corn, So turn the wheel round so bon-ny!____

There was an owd yowe wi' only one horn,
Fifty naw me nonny!
And she picked up her living among the green corn,
So turn the wheel round so bonny!

One day said the pindar to his man,
'Oh dear, Johnny!
I prithee go pen that owd yowe if tha can.'
So turn the wheel round so bonny!

So off went the man to pen this owd yowe,
Fifty naw me nonny!
She knocked him three times among the green corn,
So turn the wheel round so bonny!

Then the butcher was sent for to take this yowe's life,
Fifty naw me nonny!
And along come the butcher a-whetting his knife,
So turn the wheel round so bonny!

The owd yowe she started a-whetting her pegs,
Fifty naw me nonny!
She run at the butcher and broke both his legs,
So turn the wheel round so bonny!

This owd yowe was sent to fight for the king,
Fifty naw me nonny!
She killed horsemen and footmen just as they came in,
So turn the wheel round so bonny!

OXFORD CITY

Sung by Mr Harper, King's Lynn, Norfolk (R.V.W. 1905)

In__ Ox - ford ci - ty lived a__ la - dy, And she was beau - ti - ful and fair. Oh, she was court - ed by__ a__ sail - or, And he did__ love her as his dear.

In Oxford City lived a lady,
And she was beautiful and fair.
Oh, she was courted by a sailor,
And he did love her as his dear.

He said: 'My dear, let us get married,
Let us now no longer stay.
I'll work for you both late and early
If you my wedded bride will be.'

This girl she loved him, but at a distance.
She did not seem to be quite so fond.
He said: 'My dear, you seem to slight me.
I'm sure you love some other man.'

He saw her dancing with some other.
A jealous thought came to his mind;
And to destroy his own true lover,
He gave to her a glass of wine.

So soon she drank it, so soon she felt it.
'Oh, hold me fast, my dear,' said she.
'Is it that glass of wine you gave me
That takes my innocent life away?'

'That glass of wine now which I gave you,
That glass of wine did strong poison hide,
For if you won't be my true lover,
You'll never be no other man's bride.

'That glass of wine now which I gave you,
Oh, I have drinked of the same,' said he.
'So in each other's arms we'll die together,
To warn young men of jealousy.'

'Oh hark, oh hark, the cocks are crowing.
The daylight now will soon appear,
And into my cold grave I'm going,
And it's you, Willie, as called me there.'

THE PLOUGHMAN

Sung by Mr Henry Burstow, Horsham, Sussex (R.V.W. 1904)

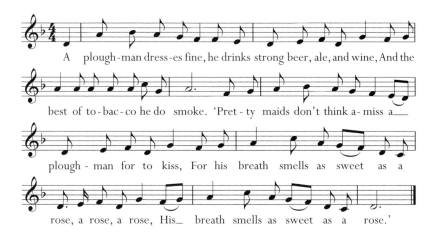

A ploughman dresses fine, he drinks strong beer, ale, and wine,
And the best of tobacco he do smoke.
'Pretty maids don't think amiss a ploughman for to kiss,
For his breath smells as sweet as a rose, a rose, a rose,
His breath smells as sweet as a rose.'

A ploughman in his shirt he completely does his work,
And so loudly to the little boy do call,
Saying: 'Be nimble and be quick by the swishing of your whip.'
And so merrily he'll rattle them along, along, along,
And so merrily he'll rattle them along.

When our shears are shod, to the blacksmith off we wad,
And so loudly to the blacksmith we do call,
Saying: 'Be nimble and be quick, and throw your blows in thick.'
And so merrily he will swing his hammer round, around, around,
And so merrily he'll swing his hammer round.

When our shears are done, to the ale-house we will run,
And so loudly to the landlord we do call;
Saying: 'Bring to us some beer, for while I am here,
A ploughman is always a-dry, a-dry, a-dry,
A ploughman is always a-dry.'

RATCLIFFE HIGHWAY

Sung by Mrs Betty Howard, King's Lynn, Norfolk (R.V.W. 1905)

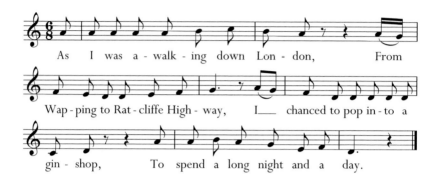

As I was a-walk-ing down Lon-don, From Wap-ping to Rat-cliffe High-way, I__ chanced to pop in-to a gin-shop, To spend a long night and a day.

As I was a-walking down London,
From Wapping to Ratcliffe Highway,
I chanced to pop into a gin-shop,
To spend a long night and a day.

A young doxy came rolling up to me,
And asked if I'd money to sport.
For a bottle of wine changed a guinea,
And she quickly replied: 'That's the sort.'

When the bottle was put on the table,
There was glasses for everyone.
When I asked for the change of my guinea,
She tipped me a verse of her song.

This lady flew into a passion,
And placed both her hands on her hip,
Saying: 'Sailor, don't you know our
  fashion?
Do you think you're on board of your
  ship?'

'If this is your fashion to rob me,
Such a fashion I'll never abide.
So launch out the change of my guinea,
Or else I'll give you a broadside.'

A gold watch hung over the mantel,
So the change of my guinea I take,
And down the stairs I run nimbly,
Saying: 'Darn my old boots, I'm well paid.'

The night being dark in my favour,
To the river I quickly did creep,
And I jumped in a boat bound for
  Deptford,
And got safe aboard of my ship.

So come all you bold young sailors,
That ramble down Ratcliffe Highway,
If you chance to pop into a gin-shop,
Beware, lads, how long you do stay.

For the songs and the liquors invite you,
And your heart will be all in a rage;
If you give them a guinea for a bottle,
You can go to the devil for change.

THE RED HERRING

Sung by Mr John Trump, North Petherton, Somerset (C.J.S. 1906)

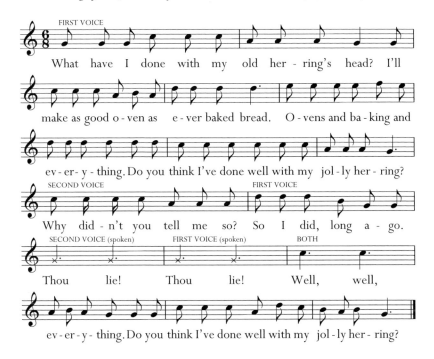

What have I done with my old herring's head?
I'll make as good oven as ever baked bread.
Ovens and baking and everything.
Do you think I've done well with my jolly herring?
　　　2nd Voice: Why didn't you tell me so?
　　　1st Voice: So I did, long ago.
(*Spoken*) *2nd Voice*: Thou lie!
 (*Spoken*) *1st Voice*: Thou lie!
Well, well, everything.
Do you think I've done well with my jolly herring?

What have I made with my old herring's eyes?
Forty jackdaws and fifty magpies,
Linnets and larks and everything.
Do you think I've done well with my jolly herring?

What have I made of my old herring's ribs?
Blooming great tower and a blooming great bridge.
Bridges, towers, and everything.
Do you think I've done well with my jolly herring?

What have I made of my old herring's guts?
Forty bright women and fifty bright sluts,
Wantons and sluts and everything.
Do you think I've done well with my jolly herring?

What have I made of my old herring's navel?
As good a wheelbarrow as ever drawed gravel,
Wheelbarrow, shovel, and everything.
Do you think I've done well with my jolly herring?

What have I made of my old herring's tail?
I'll make as good ship as ever set sail,
Sailcloth, rigging, and everything.
Do you think I've done well with my jolly herring?

ROBIN HOOD AND THE PEDLAR

Sung by Mr Peter Verrall, Horsham, Sussex (R. V. W. 1906)

It's___ of a ped - lar,___ ped - lar bold, A
ped - lar bold there chanced to be. He took his pack all___
on his back, And___ mer - ri - ly trudged o'er the lea.

It's of a pedlar, pedlar bold,
A pedlar bold there chanced to be.
He took his pack all on his back,
And merrily trudged o'er the lea.

By chance he met two troublesome men,
Two troublesome men they chanced to be;
The one of them was bold Robin Hood,
And the other was Little John so free.

'O pedlar, pedlar, what's in thy pack?
Come speedily and tell to me.'
'I've several suits of the gay green cloth,
And silken bowstrings by two and three.'

'If you've several suits of the gay green cloth,
And silken bowstrings two or three,
Then by my body,' cries Little John,
'One half your pack shall belong to me.'

'Oh no, oh no,' says the pedlar bold,
'Oh no, oh no, that never can be,
For there's never a man from fair Nottingham
Can take one half my pack from me.'

Then the pedlar he pulled off his pack,
And put it a little below his knee,
Saying: 'If you do move me one perch from this,
My pack and all shall go with thee.'

Then Little John he drew his sword,
The pedlar by his pack did stand,
They fought until they both did sweat,
And John cried: 'Pedlar, pray hold your hand.'

Then Robin Hood he was standing by,
And he did laugh most heartily,
'I could find a man of smaller scale,
Could thrash the pedlar and also thee.'

'Go you try, master,' says Little John,
'And go you try most speedily,
For by my body,' says Little John,
'I'm sure this night you will know me.'

Then Robin Hood he drew his sword,
And the pedlar by his pack did stand;
They fought till the blood in streams did flow,
Till he cried: 'Pedlar, pray hold your hand.

'Oh pedlar, pedlar, what is thy name?
Come speedily and tell to me.'
'Well now, my name I never will tell
Till both your names you have told me.'

'The one of us is bold Robin Hood,
And the other is Little John so free.'
'Now,' says the pedlar, 'it lays to my good will
Whether my name I choose to tell thee.

'I'm Gamble Gold of the gay green woods,
And travelled far beyond the sea.
For killing a man in my father's land,
Far from my country I was forced to flee.'

'If you're Gamble Gold of the gay green woods,
And travelled far beyond the sea,
You are my mother's own sister's son,
What nearer cousins can we be?'

They sheathed their swords with friendly words,
So merrily they did agree.
They went to a tavern and there they dined,
And crackèd bottles most merrily.

ROUNDING THE HORN

Sung by Mr William Bolton, Southport, Lancashire (A.G.G. May 1907)

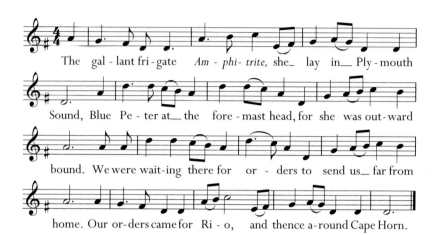

The gal-lant fri-gate Am-phi-trite, she_ lay in_ Ply-mouth Sound, Blue Pe-ter at_ the fore-mast head, for she was out-ward bound. We were wait-ing there for or-ders to send us_ far from home. Our or-ders came for Ri-o, and thence a-round Cape Horn.

The gallant frigate *Amphitrite*, she lay in Plymouth Sound,
Blue Peter at the fore-mast head, for she was outward bound.
We were waiting there for orders to send us far from home.
Our orders came for Rio*, and thence around Cape Horn.

When we arrived at Rio, we prepared for heavy gales;
We set up all our rigging, boys, and bent on all new sails.
From ship to ship they cheered us as we did sail along,
And wished us pleasant weather in rounding of Cape Horn.

When beating off Magellan Straits it blew exceeding hard,
While shortening sail, two gallant tars fell from the tops'l yard.
By angry seas the ropes we threw from their poor hands was torn,
We were forced to leave them to the sharks that prowl around Cape Horn.

When we got round the Horn, my boys, we had some glorious days,
And very soon our killick dropped in Valparaiso Bay.
The pretty girls came down in flocks, I solemnly declare
They're far before the Plymouth girls with their long and curly hair.

They love a jolly sailor when he spends his money free;
They'll laugh and sing and merry, merry be, and have a jovial spree.
And when your money is all gone, they won't on you impose;
They are not like the Plymouth girls that'll pawn and sell your clothes.

Farewell to Valparaiso, and farewell for a while.
Likewise to all the Spanish girls along the coast of Chile*.
And if ever I live to be paid off, I'll sit and sing this song:
'God bless those pretty Spanish girls we left around Cape Horn.'

* 'Rio' is pronounced 'Rye-o', and Mr Bolton sang 'Chile' to rhyme with
'while'.

THE ROYAL OAK

Sung by Mr Moses Mansfield, Almshouse Cottages, Haslemere, Surrey (C.C. 1912)

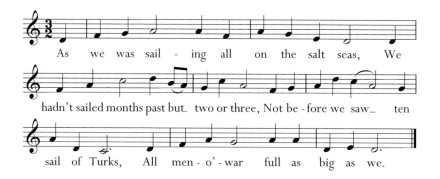

As we was sail - ing all on the salt seas, We hadn't sailed months past but_ two or three, Not be - fore we saw_ ten sail of Turks, All men - o' - war full as big as we.

As we was sailing all on the salt seas,
We hadn't sailed months past but two or three,
Not before we saw ten sail of Turks,
All men-o'-war full as big as we.

'Pull down your colours, you English dogs!
Pull down your colours, do not refuse.
Oh, pull down your colours, you English dogs,
Or else your precious life you'll lose!'

Our captain being a valiant man,
And a well-bespoken young man were he:
'Oh, it never shall be said that we died like dogs,
But we will fight them most manfully!'

'Go up, you lofty cabin boys,
And mount the mainmast topsail high,
For to spread abroad to King George's fleet
That we'll run the risk or else we'll die!'

The fight begun 'bout six in the morning,
And on to the setting of the sun.
Oh, and at the rising of the next morning,
Out of ten ships we couldn't see but one.

Oh, three we sank and three we burned,
And three we caused to run away,
And one we brought into Portsmouth harbour,
For to let them know we had won the day.

If anyone then should enquire
Or want to know our captain's name,
Oh, Captain Wellfounder's our chief commander
But the *Royal Oak* is our ship by name.

59

THE SAILOR FROM DOVER

Sung by Mrs Lucy Durston, Bridgwater, Somerset (C.J.S. 1909)

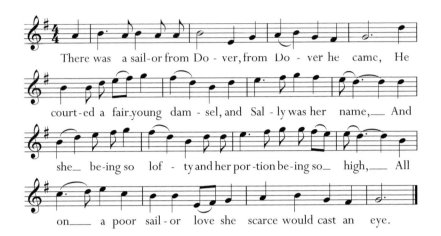

There was a sailor from Dover, from Dover he came,
He courted a fair young damsel, and Sally was her name,
And she being so lofty and her portion being so high,
All on a poor sailor love she scarce would cast an eye.

'O Sally, dearest Sally, O Sally,' then said he,
'I fear that your false heart my ruin it will be;
Without your present hatred is turnèd into love,
You'll make me broken-hearted and my ruin it will prove.'

'I cannot love a sailor, nor any such a man,
So keep your heart in comfort and forget me if you can.
I pray you keep your distance and mind your own discourse,
For I never intend to marry you unless that I am forced.'

But when a year was over and twelve months they was past,
This lovely young damsel she grew sick in love at last.
Entangled she was all in her love, she did not know for why,
So she sent for the young man on whom she had an eye.

'Oh, am I now now the doctor, that you have sent for me?
Pray don't you well remember how once you slighted me?
How once you slighted me, my love, and treated me with scorn?
So now I will reward you for all that you have done.'

'For what is past and gone,' she said, 'I pray you to forgive,
And grant me just a little longer time for to live.'
'Oh no, my dearest Sally, as long as I have breath,
I'll dance all on your grave, love, as you lie under the earth.'

A Sailor in the North Country

Sung by Mrs Harriet Verrall, Horsham, Sussex (R.V.W. 1904)

A sailor in the north country,
He had a most beautiful wife.
Her courage was so great and her temper
  more than sweet,
And the sailor he loved her as his life.

As they were walking out one day,
They met a noble captain on the way,
Kind obedience to the maid! But she
  bowed and nothing said,
'Twas her beauty did the captain's heart
  betray.

The captain to his house then he goes,
And sent for the sailor straight away,
'My business runs so: to the West Indies
  you must go,
In the morning, or by the break of day.'

'To obey the noble Master I will go,
On the sea, to venture my life.'
But little did he dream the captain's heart
  was so inflamed,
On the charms of his most beautiful wife.

The sailor to his wife then he goes,
And kissed her and called her his dear.
'Bad news I have to tell you, I must bid
  you farewell,
In the morning when daylight does
  appear.'

As soon as she heard him say so,
She wrung her hands and bitterly did cry,
She kissed him and said: 'My dear Jimmy
  I'm afraid
You'll be drowned in the raging ocean
  wide.'

The hour and the moment did come,
The poor sailor no longer could stay
To hear his wife lament till his heart was
  discontent.
He kissed her and went weeping away.

He had only been gone two days or three
On the seas for to venture his life,
Before the captain came with his heart in
  great flame,
To seize on the poor sailor's wife.

'Your pardon, dear lady,' he cried,
'Your pardon, dear lady, if you please,
Your pardon if you please, for 'tis you
  can give me ease
One night to enjoy your sweet charms.'

'Oh, are you any lord, duke, or king,
Or are you any ruler of the land?
The King shall lose his crown before at
  my feet you shall lie down,
Or before I will be at your command.

' 'Twas only one twelve-month ago
That I was made your man Jimmy's bride,
It's pleasing to my lot, the best husband I have got,
I'll be constant unto him for life.'

A Sailor's Life

Sung by Mr Henry Hills (late of Lodsworth, Sussex), at Shepperton, Middlesex (W.P.M. 1899)

A sailor's life is a merry life.
They rob young girls of their heart's delight,
Leaving them behind to sigh and mourn.
They never know when they will return.

Here's four and twenty all in a row.
My sweetheart cuts the brightest show;
He's proper, tall, genteel withal,
And if I don't have him I'll have none at all.

O father, fetch me a little boat,
That I might on the ocean float,
And every Queen's ship that we pass by,
We'll make enquire for my sailor boy.

We had not sailed long upon the deep,
Before a Queen's ship we chanced to meet.
'You sailors all, come tell me true,
Does my sweet William sail among your crew?'

'Oh no, fair lady, he is not here,
For he is drowned, we greatly fear.
On yon green island as we passed by,
There we lost sight of your sailor boy.'

She wrung her hands and she tore her hair,
Much like a woman in great despair.
Her little boat 'gainst a rock did run.
'How can I live now my William is gone?'

SALISBURY PLAIN

Sung by Mr and Mrs Verrall, Horsham, Sussex (R.V.W. 1904)

As I walked over Salisbury Plain,
Oh, there I met a scamping young blade.
He kissed me and enticèd me so
Till along with him I was forced for to go.

We came unto a public house at last,
And there for man and wife we did pass.
He called for ale and wine and strong
  beer,
Till at length we both to bed did repair.

'Undress yourself, my darling,' says he.
'Undress yourself, and come to bed with
  me.'
'Oh yes, that I will,' then says she,
'If you'll keep all those flash girls away.'

'Those flash girls you need not fear,
For you'll be safe-guarded, my dear.
I'll maintain you as some lady so gay,
For I'll go a-robbing on the highway.'

Early next morning my love he arose,
And so nimbly he put on his clothes.
Straight to the highway he set sail,
And 'twas there he robbed the coaches
  of the mail.

Oh, it's now my love in Newgate Jail
  do lie,
Expecting every moment to die.
The Lord have mercy on his poor soul,
For I think I hear the death-bell for to
  toll.

THE SHIP IN DISTRESS

Sung by Mr Harwood, Watersfield, Pulborough, Sussex (G.B. 1907)

You seamen bold who plough the ocean
See dangers landsmen never know.
It's not for honour and promotion;
No tongue can tell what they undergo.
In the blusterous wind and the great dark
   water
Our ship went drifting on the sea,
Her headgear gone, and her rudder
   broken,
Which brought us to extremity.

For fourteen days, heartsore and hungry,
Seeing but wild water and bitter sky,
Poor fellows, they stood in a totter,
A-casting lots as to which should die.
The lot it fell on Robert Jackson,
Whose family was so very great.
'I'm free to die, but oh, my comrades,
Let me keep look-out till the break of day.'

A full-dressed ship like the sun a-glittering
Came bearing down to their relief.
As soon as this glad news was shouted,
It banished all their care and grief.
The ship brought to, no longer drifting,
Safe in Saint Vincent, Cape Verde, she gained.
You seamen all, who hear my story,
Pray you'll never suffer the like again.

SIX DUKES WENT A-FISHING

Sung by Mr George Gouldthorpe, Brigg Union Workhouse, Lincolnshire (P.G. 1906)

Six dukes went a-fishing
Down by yon sea-side.
One of them spied a dead body
Lain by the waterside.

The one said to the other,
These words I heard them say:
'It's the Royal Duke of Grantham
That the tide has washed away.'

They took him up to Portsmouth,
To a place where was known;
From there up to London,
To the place where he was born.

They took out his bowels,
And stretched out his feet,
And they balmed his body
With roses so sweet.

Six dukes stood before him,
Twelve raised him from the ground,
Nine lords followed after him,
In their black mourning gown.

Black was their mourning,
And white were the wands,
And so yellow were the flamboys
That they carried in their hands.

He now lies betwixt two towers,
He now lies in cold clay,
And the Royal Queen of Grantham
Went weeping away.

THE STREAMS OF LOVELY NANCY

Sung by Mr George Dowden, Lackington, Piddlehinton, Dorset (H.E.D.H. & R.F.F.H. 1905)

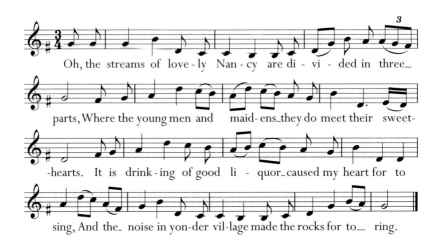

Oh, the streams of lovely Nancy are divided in three parts,
Where the young men and maidens they do meet their sweethearts.
It is drinking of good liquor caused my heart for to sing,
And the noise in yonder village made the rocks for to ring.

At the top of this mountain, there my love's castle stands.
It's all overbuilt with ivory on yonder black sand,
Fine arches, fine porches, and diamonds so bright.
It's a pilot for a sailor on a dark winter's night.

On yonder high mountain, where the wild fowl do fly,
There is one amongst them that flies very high.
If I had her in my arms, love, near the diamond's black land,
How soon I'd secure her by the sleight of my hand.

At the bottom of this mountain there runs a river clear.
A ship from the Indies did once anchor there,
With her red flags a-flying and the beating of her drum,
Sweet instruments of music and the firing of her gun.

So come all you little streamers that walk the meadows gay,
I'll write unto my own true love, wherever she may be.
For her rosy lips entice me, with her tongue she tells me 'No',
And an angel might direct us right, and where shall we go?

The Trees They Grow So High

Sung by unnamed woman singer, Stoke Fleming, Devon (B.B. n.d.)

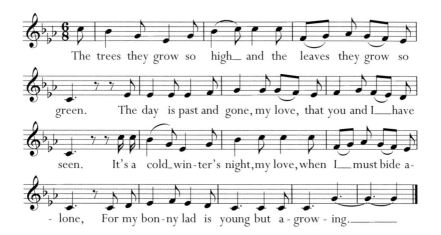

The trees they grow so high and the leaves they grow so green.
The day is past and gone, my love, that you and I have seen.
It's a cold winter's night, my love, when I must bide alone,
For my bonny lad is young but a-growing.

As I was a-walking by yonder church wall,
I saw four and twenty young men a-playing at the ball.
I asked for my own true love but they would not let him come,
For they said the boy was young, but a-growing.

'O father, dearest father, you've done to me much wrong.
You've tied me to a boy when you know he is too young.'
'O daughter, dearest daughter, if you'll wait a little while,
A lady you shall be, while he's growing.

'We'll send your love to college, all for a year or two,
And then perhaps in time the boy will do for you.
I'll buy you white ribbons to tie about his waist,
To let the ladies know that he's married.'

And so early in the morning at the dawning of the day,
They went out into the hayfield to have some sport and play,
And what they did there, she never would declare,
But she never more complained of his growing.

And at the age of sixteen he was a married man,
And at the age of seventeen she brought to him a son,
And at the age of eighteen the grass grew over him,
And that soon put an end to his growing.

THE WHALE-CATCHERS

Sung by Mr Henry Hills (late of Lodsworth, Sussex), at Shepperton, Middlesex (W.P.M. 1900)

On the twen-ty-third of March, my boys, We hoist-ed our top-sail, Cry-ing: 'Heav'n a-bove pro-tect us With a sweet and a plea-sant gale.' We ne-ver was down-heart-ed Nor let our cour-age fail, But bore a-way up to Green-land For to catch the Green-land whale, For to catch the Green-land whale.

On the twenty-third of March, my boys,
We hoisted our topsail,
Crying: 'Heav'n above protect us
With a sweet and a pleasant gale.'
We never was down-hearted
Nor let our courage fail,
But bore away up to Greenland
For to catch the Greenland whale,
For to catch the Greenland whale.

And when we came to Greenland
Where the bitter winds did blow,
We tacked about all in the north
Among the frost and snow.
Our finger-tops were frozen off,
And likewise our toe-nails,
As we crawled on the deck, my boys,
Looking out for the Greenland whale,
Looking out for the Greenland whale.

And when we came to Imez,
Where the mountains flowed with snow,
We tacked about all in the north
Till we heard a whalefish blow.
And when we catch this whale, brave boys,
Homeward we will steer.
We'll make the valleys ring, my boys,
A-drinking of strong beer.
 We'll make those lofty alehouses
 In London town to roar;
 And when our money is all gone,
 To Greenland go for more,
 To Greenland go for more.

WHEN I WAS A LITTLE BOY

Sung by Mr John Stickle, Baltasound, Unst, Shetland (P.S.-S. 1947)

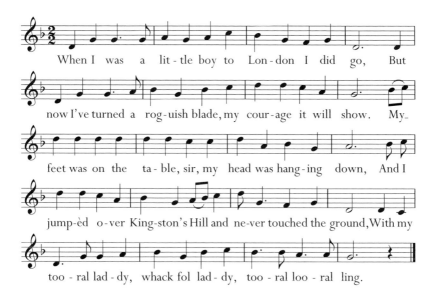

When I was a little boy to London I did go,
But now I've turned a roguish blade, my courage it will show.
My feet was on the table, sir, my head was hanging down,
And I jumpèd over Kingston's Hill and never touched the ground,
    With my tooral laddy, whack fol laddy, tooral looral ling.

I bought myself a little bull about three inches high;
The people all admired me, it's for to hear him cry.
The people all admired me for he made such an awful sound,
He made the steeple of St Paul's Church come tumbling to the ground,
    With my, etc.

I bought myself a flock of sheep and most of them were wethers;
Sometimes they brought me fine wool, sometimes they brought me feathers.
They were as fine a flock, sir, as anyone could possess,
For every month or six weeks' time they brought me six lambs apiece,
    With my, etc.

I bought myself a little hen, and of her I took great care;
I set her on a mussel shell and she hatched me out a hare.
The hare grew up a milk-white steed about eighteen yards high,
And if anyone tell you a bigger story, I'll tell you it's a bloody lie.
    With my, etc.

I bought myself a little box about three acres square;
I stowed it into my breeches pocket, the guineas they were there.
Now the people all admired me, thanked me for what I'd done,
And they gave me a portion of silver and gold about ten thousand ton,
    With my, etc.

WHEN I WAS YOUNG

Sung by Mrs Moore, High Heworth, County Durham (W.G.W. 1920)

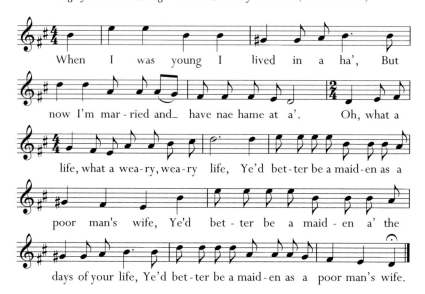

When I was young I lived in a ha',
But now I'm married and have nae hame at a'.
  Oh, what a life, what a weary, weary life,
  Ye'd better be a maiden as a poor man's wife,
  Ye'd better be a maiden a' the days of your life,
  Ye'd better be a maiden as a poor man's wife.

When I was young I used to sport and play,
But now I'm married and the cradle's in the way.
  Oh, what a life, etc.

When I was young I wore my slippers thin,
But now I'm married and the water it runs in.
  Oh, what a life, etc.

YE MAR'NERS ALL

Sung by Mrs Marina Russell, Upwey, Dorset (H.E.D.H. & R.F.F.H. 1907)

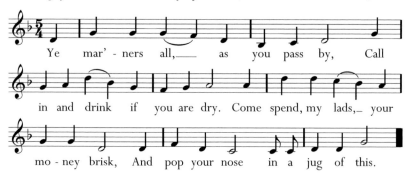

Ye mar'ners all, as you pass by,
Call in and drink if you are dry.
Come spend, my lads, your moncy brisk,
And pop your nose in a jug of this.

Oh, mar'ners all, if you've half a crown,
You're welcome all for to sit down.
Come spend, my lads, your money brisk,
And pop your nose in a jug of this.

Oh, tipplers all, as ye pass by,
Come in and drink if you are dry.
Call in and drink, think not amiss,
And pop your nose in a jug of this.

Oh, now I'm old and can scarcely crawl,
I've an old grey beard and a head that's bald,
Crown my desire and fulfill my bliss,
A pretty girl and a jug of this.

Oh, when I'm in my grave and dead,
And all my sorrows are past and fled,
Transform me then into a fish,
And let me swim in a jug of this.

THE YOUNG AND SINGLE SAILOR

Sung by Mr Burridge (Burrage), 'Rushetts', near Capel, Surrey (R.V.W. 1908)

A fair maid walked all in her garden.
A brisk young sailor she chanced to spy.
He stepped up to her, thinking to view her.
Says he: 'Fair maid, could you fancy me?'

'Oh no, young man, you're a man of honour,
A man of honour you seem to be.
So don't impose on a poor young woman
Who is scarce fitted your servant to be.'

'If you tell me you're a poor young woman,
The more regard I shall have for you.
So come with me and I'll make you happy,
And you'll have servants for to wait on you.'

'Oh no, young man, I have a sweetheart,
And seven long years he's away from me,
And seven more I will wait for him,
And if he's alive he will return to me.'

'Oh, seven years makes an alteration.
Perhaps he's drowned and is now at rest.'
'Then no other man shall ever join me,
For he's the darling boy that I love best.'

He put his hand all in his pocket,
His fingers being both long and small,
Saying: 'Here's the ring, love, we broke between us.'
Soon as she saw it, then she down did fall.

He took her close all in his arrums,
He gave her kisses by one, two, three,
Saying: 'I'm your young and single sailor,
That has come home for to marry thee.'

YOUNG EDWIN IN THE LOWLANDS LOW

Sung by Mrs Hopkins, Axford, Basingstoke, Hampshire (G.B.G. & C.G. 1907, R.V.W 1909)

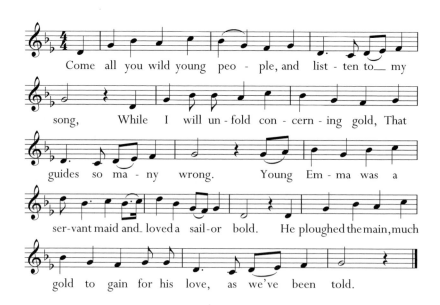

Come all you wild young peo - ple, and list - ten to__ my
song, While I will un - fold con - cern - ing gold, That
guides so ma - ny wrong. Young Em - ma was a
ser-vant maid and_ loved a sail-or bold. He ploughed the main, much
gold to gain for his love, as we've been told.

72

Come all you wild young people, and listen to my song,
While I will unfold concerning gold, that guides so many wrong.
Young Emma was a servant maid and loved a sailor bold.
He ploughed the main, much gold to gain for his love, as we've been told.

He ploughed the main for seven years and then he returned home.
As soon as he set foot on shore, unto his love did go.
He went unto young Emma's house, his gold all for to show,
That he had gained upon the main, all in the Lowlands low.

'My father keeps a public house down by the side of the sea,
And you go there and stay the night, and there you wait for me.
I'll meet you in the morning, but don't let my parents know
Your name it is Young Edwin that ploughed the Lowlands low.'

Young Edwin he sat drinking till time to go to bed.
He little thought a sword that night would part his body and head,
And Edwin he got into bed and scarcely was asleep,
When Emily's cruel parents soft into his room did creep.

They stabbed him, dragged him out of bed, and to the sea did go.
They sent his body floating down to the Lowlands low.
As Emily she lay sleeping, she had a dreadful dream;
She dreamed she saw Young Edwin's blood a-flowing like the stream.

'Oh father, where's the stranger come here last night to lay?'
'Oh, he is dead, no tales can tell,' her father he did say.
'Then father, cruel father, you'll die a public show,
For the murdering of Young Edwin that ploughed the Lowlands low.

'The fishes of the ocean swim o'er my lover's breast.
His body rolls in motion, I hope his soul's at rest.
The shells along the seashore that are rolling to and fro
Remind me of my Edwin that ploughed the Lowlands low.'

So many a day she passed away and tried to ease her mind,
And Emma, broken-hearted, was to Bedlam forced to go.
Crying: 'Oh, my friends, my love is gone, and I am left behind.'
Her shrieks were for Young Edwin that ploughed the Lowlands low.

THE YOUNG GIRL CUT DOWN IN HER PRIME

Sung by an unnamed singer, East Meon, Hampshire (F.J. 1909)

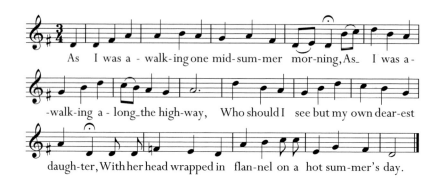

As I was a-walking one midsummer morning,
As I was a-walking along the highway,
Who should I see but my own dearest daughter,
With her head wrapped in flannel on a hot summer's day.

'O mother, dear mother, come set you down by me.
Come set you down by me and pity my case;
For my wounds are now aching, my poor heart is breaking,
And I'm in low spirits and surely must die.

'O mother, dear mother, come send for the clergyman,
O send for the doctor to bind up my wound,
And likewise my young man, whose heart it did wander,
That he may see me before I'm screwed down.

'And when I am dead to the churchyard they'll bear me,
Six jolly fellows to carry me on,
And in each of their hands a bunch of green laurel,
So they may not smell me as they're walking along.

'So rattle your drums and play your fife over me,
So rattle your drums as we march along.
Then return to your home and think on that young girl:
"Oh, there goes a young girl cut down in her prime."'

LIST OF COLLECTORS

A.G.G.	Anne G. Gilchrist	H.E.D.H.	Henry E. D. Hammond
B.B.	Bertha Bidder	J.B.	Janet Broadwood
C.C.	Clive Carey	J.F.G.	J. F. Guyer
C.G.	Charles Gamblin	J.E.T.	J. E. Thomas
C.J.S.	Cecil J. Sharp	L.E.B.	Lucy Broadwood
E.B.	Ella Bull	M.E.S.	Mary E. Spence
E.J.M.	E. J. Moeran	M.S.	Marie Slocombe
E.M.L.	Ella M. Leather	P.G.	Percy Grainger
E.T.S.	E. T. Sweeting	P.S.S.	Patrick Shuldham-Shaw
F.M.C.	Francis M. Collinson	R.F.F.H.	Robert F. F. Hammond
F.J.	Francis Jekyll	R.V.W.	Ralph Vaughan Williams
G.B.	George Butterworth	T.A.	Tilly Aston
G.B.G.	George B. Gardiner	W.F.	Walter Ford
G.E.McC.	G. E. McCleay	W.G.W.	W. G. Whittaker
H.B.G.	H. Balfour Gardiner	W.P.M.	W. Percy Merrick

NOTES ON THE SONGS

[The original notes have been supplemented for this new edition; new material is shown separately. Space prohibits the inclusion of exhaustive references to further published examples of songs, so these have been restricted, in the main, to versions which have appeared in the *Journals* and in other EFDSS publications, together with a small number of other particularly relevant books; Roy Palmer's collections have been especially useful. Roud and, where appropriate, Laws and Child classification numbers have been added for each song, and the interested reader can make use of Steve Roud's invaluable folk song and broadside databases to locate more song variants; the Roud Index is available by subscription, or can be consulted at institutions such as the Vaughan Williams Memorial Library at Cecil Sharp House.

The importance of the Broadside press in the transmission (and, sometimes, origination) of folk song is more widely recognised today than it was by many of the collectors of the early twentieth century. The majority of the songs in this book were published on broadside song sheets at one time or another, sometimes in forms very close to those in which they were later noted from singers. One of the country's principal collections of broadsides, that held at the Bodleian Library of the University of Oxford, is now available via the internet, and images of most of the collection can be seen at the library's website; it is, in practice, more readily accessible than are many of the books cited here. References to examples are given by title and/or shelf-mark.]

ABBREVIATIONS

(For the convenience of readers who may already be accustomed to using the invaluable *Guide to English Folk Song Collections* by Margaret Dean-Smith, we have generally adopted the letter-signs used in that work.)

BCS	Broadwood, L. E., *English County Songs*. London, 1893.
BF	Barrett, W. A., *English Folk Songs*. London, 1891.
BGG	Baring-Gould, S., and Fleetwood Sheppard, H., *A Garland of Country Song*. London, 1895. Reprinted Felinfach: Llanerch Press, 1998.
BGS	Baring-Gould, S., and Sharp, C. J., *English Folk-Songs for Schools*. London, 1906.
BGSW	Baring-Gould, S., and others, *Songs of the West* (revised ed.). London, 1905.
Bronson	Bronson B. H., *The Traditional Tunes of the Child Ballads*. Princeton, 1959-72.
BSFL	Burne, C., *Shropshire Folk-Lore*. London, 1883.
BTSC	Broadwood, L. E., *English Traditional Songs and Carols*. London, 1908.
Child	Child, F. J., *The English and Scottish Popular Ballads*, 1882-98. Reprinted New York, Dover Publications, 1965. Revised edition Loomis House Press, 2001- (proceeding).
CPM	Chappell, W., *Popular Music of the Olden Time*. London, 1858-59.
CSB	Copper, R., *The Copper Family Song Book*. Peacehaven: Coppersongs, 1995.
CSES	Copper, R., *A Song for Every Season*. London 1971. New edition Peacehaven: Coppersongs, 1997.
DPG	Dawney, M., *The Ploughboy's Glory*. London, 1977.
ED&S	*English Dance and Song*. The magazine of the English Folk Dance and Song Society. London, 1935 -
FMJ	*Folk Music Journal* (successor to JEFDSS). London, 1965 -.
FSJ	*Journal of the Folk Song Society*. London, 1899-1931.
GFH	Gardiner, G. B., *Folk Songs from Hampshire*. London, 1909.
GOR	Gillington, A. E., *Songs of the Open Road*. London, 1911.
HGG	Hamer, F., *Garners Gay*. London, 1967.
HGGR	Hamer, F., *Green Groves*. London, 1973.
JEFDSS	*Journal of the English Folk Dance and Song Society* (successor to FSJ). London, 1931-1964.
KCSC	Karpeles, M., *Cecil Sharp's Collection of English Folk Songs*. Oxford, 1974.
KFBI	Kennedy, P., *Folksongs of Britain and Ireland*. London, 1975 and 1984.
KG	Kidson, F., *A Garland of English Folk-Songs*. London, 1926.
KP	Kidson, F., *English Peasant Songs*. London, 1929.

KTT   Kidson, F., *Traditional Tunes*. Oxford, 1891. Reprinted Felinfach: Llanerch Press, 1999.

MSS   Moeran, E. J., *Six Suffolk Folk Songs*. London, 1932.

ODNR   Opie, I. and P., *The Oxford Dictionary of Nursery Rhymes*. Oxford, 1951.

PBB   Palmer, R., *Everyman's Book of British Ballads*. London, 1980. Reprinted as *A Book of British Ballads*, Felinfach: Llanerch Press, 1998.

PBC   Palmer, R., *Boxing the Compass*. Todmorden, Herron Publications, 2001. A revised and expanded edition of *The Oxford Book of Sea Songs* (Oxford, 1986). Page references are to the new edition.

PCL   Purslow, F., *The Constant Lovers*. London, 1972.

PECS   Palmer, R., *Everyman's Book of English Country Songs*. London, 1979. Reprinted as *The English Country Songbook*, Omnibus Press, 1986.

REC   Reeves, J., *The Everlasting Circle*. London, 1960.

RIP   Reeves, J., *The Idiom of the People*. London, 1958.

PFD   Purslow, F., *The Foggy Dew*. London, 1974.

PMB   Purslow, F., *Marrow Bones*. London, 1965.

PRVW   Palmer, R., *Folk Songs Collected by Ralph Vaughan Williams*. London, 1983. Reprinted as *Bushes and Briars: Folk Songs Collected by Ralph Vaughan Williams*, Felinfach: Llanerch Press, 1999.

PWS   Purslow, F., *The Wanton Seed*. London, 1968.

S100   Sharp, C., *One Hundred English Folksongs*. Boston, 1916. Reprinted New York: Dover, 1975.

SEF (I-II)   Sharp, C. J., *English Folk Songs*. London, 1921.

SFS (I-V)   Sharp, C. J., and (for Series I-III) Marson, C. L., *Folk Songs from Somerset*. London, 1904-9.

SLM   Stubbs, K., *The Life of a Man*. London, 1970.

SYM   O'Shaughnessy, P., *Yellowbelly Ballads*. Lincoln, 1975, 2 vols.

VWE   Vaughan Williams, R., *Folk Songs from the Eastern Counties*. London, 1908.

WSS   Whall, W. B., *Sea Songs and Shanties* (revised ed.). Glasgow, 1920.

WUP   Williams, A., *Folk Songs of the Upper Thames*. London, 1923.

[Substantial additions have been made to the list of works cited. Where these are books published after Dean-Smith's *Guide* of 1954, letter-signs have been coined using her format. References in the notes to the *Journals* have been expanded to include issue number (bracketed) and date of publication.]

All Things are Quite Silent

(FSJ II (8) 1906 202) Roud 2532

Even in Nelson's day, when the sailor with his tarry pigtail was the nation's pride, so notorious were conditions aboard the royal ships that the Navy could only be maintained by pressing men to sea. The press-gangs were the terror to life along the coasts of England, tearing men from the seamen's tavern or the plough, or even (some songs tell us) from the marriage bed, to serve in the warships with no prospect of release till the end of the war, whenever that might be. Here is one among many lamentations of wives bereft of their husbands by the press-gang. The song presumably belongs to a period before 1835, for by that time the system had almost faded out, though it was never actually abolished by Act of Parliament. This seems to be the only version of the song reported from oral tradition.

[Roy Palmer (PRVW 149) reports a broadside edition entitled *I'll Mourn for my Sailor; Or, The Compulsion*, issued by J. Ferraby, Butchery, Hull.]

As Sylvie was Walking

(JEFDSS I (1) 1932 52) Roud 170

This song was sent to W. P. Merrick from Australia. The singer, an eighty-year-old woman born near Coleford, Gloucestershire, had been living in the Antipodes since 1855. She learned the song from her uncle, also from Gloucestershire. The text has been amplified from versions sung to H. E. D. Hammond in 1906 by two Dorset women, Mrs [Jane] Hann of Stoke Abbot and Mrs [Marina] Russell of Upwey. A version from [James Parsons of] Lew Down, Devonshire [1888] appears in BGSW 78-9 under the title of *A Maiden Sat a-Weeping*.

[The final verse given here does not appear in any of the *Journal* sources, and appears to have been adapted from BGSW. The Dorset versions appeared in JFSS III (11) 1907 91-2, and two Somerset variants, noted by Cecil Sharp from Henry Tidmore, Wedmore, (1907) and George Say, Axbridge, (1908) are in FSJ V (18) 1914 62-4. Another, learned by Maurice Ogg from Edith Leaning of Coleby, Lincolnshire, was printed in ED&S 43 (2) 1981 7. The tune seems first to have been published in Charles Coffey's ballad-opera *The Beggar's Wedding* (1729), entitled *Once I Had a Sweet-Heart*, and a little later (c.1735) in Daniel Wright's *Compleat Tutor for ye Flute*, where it appears in a form very similar to Mrs Aston's. For a broadside edition, see Bodleian, Firth c.18(28): *Bunch of Green Ribbons*.]

The Banks of Green Willow

(FSJ II (6) 1905 34) Roud 172 Child 24

There is a common superstition, older than Jonah, that the presence of a wrongdoer aboard ship may make the vessel unmanageable. Disaster may result unless the offender is discovered and thrown overboard. A Scottish text printed in 1827 [*Bonnie Annie*, in *Kinloch's Ancient Scottish Ballads*; quoted in Child I 245-6, No. 24A] makes it clear that the 'Jonah' motive lies within this song, though the twentieth-century versions are so disordered that the meaning is rather obscured. The full story concerns a young woman who robs her parents, at her lover's request, and sails away with him. During a storm at sea the woman gives birth to a baby. The sailors fear that someone aboard is flying from retribution. The blame is fixed on the woman, and to her lover's grief she is thrown overboard. Later versions, however, make it seem that the lover is the murderer. Fifty years ago Sharp reported the song 'very generally sung throughout Somerset'. Five of Sharp's nine Somerset versions are given in FSJ II (6) 33-6, and FSJ III (13) 1909 292 has a Hampshire version noted by [George Gardiner and] R. Vaughan Williams.

[Parts of a few lines have been interpolated from other versions noted by Sharp and printed in FSJ II; verse four is from William Spearing, Ile Bruers, 1904. Mrs Overd's third verse, omitted here, was:

O hush your tongue you silly girl,
O hush your tongue you huzzy,
For I can do as much for thee
As any woman can for thee.

Frank Purslow, PCL 115, points out that 'banks of green willow' is a corruption of the earlier 'banks of Yarrow'. Vaughan Williams' 1909 phonograph recording of *Banks of Green Willow*, sung by David Clements, can be heard on *A Century of Song: A Celebration of Traditional Singers Since 1898* (EFDSS CD02, 1998). Other versions appear in FMJ III (2) 1976 103-4; DPG 12; PCL 4; PRVW 51 (David Clements), and *Still Growing* (EFDSS 2003) 61 (Elizabeth Mogg). See also Bronson I 298-304.]

The Banks of Newfoundland

(FSJ VIII (32) 1928 99) Roud 1812 Laws K25

Cecil Sharp collected a version of this song from a seaman [Harry Perrey]

aboard the American liner S.S. *St Paul*, in 1915 (FSJ V (20) 1916 300-1). Sharp describes it as a capstan shanty, but its use as such must have been very limited. The song seems to have been more commonly used as a forebitter or foc'sle song, sung for diversion. In both text and melody, there are remarkable similarities to some sets of the (slightly earlier) transportation ballad, *Van Diemen's Land* [Roud 221]. The incident of the dream, the names of the crew members, the detail of the good-hearted lady passenger, are all borrowed from the older ballad. Mr Farr, who was seventy-six when this song was noted from him, had a fine repertory of shanties. His text of *The Banks of Newfoundland* was almost identical with that of Sharp's informant, but we have borrowed a few phrases from the latter, also the device of the 'holystone' chorus, which, in Mr Farr's version, occurred only at the end of the song [as the second half of the final verse]. The tune is related to some Irish sets of *The Lowlands of Holland*.

[Mr Perrey's set is also printed in PBC 247-8, where Roy Palmer notes mid-nineteenth century broadside editions issued by Hodges of London and Ross of Newcastle. The song seems most often to have been found in tradition in Canada.]

The Banks Of Sweet Primroses

(FSJ IV (15) 1910 124) Roud 586

We have included this well-favoured piece as representative of a large and important class of English folk songs. Sharp found it several times in Devon and Somerset, and he includes a version from Mrs Lucy White of Hambridge in SFS I 8. In a note he mentions that the words are to be found 'on broadsides by Barraclough of Nuneaton and others'. The complete song was first printed in 1891 (BF 80). There is a North Country version in KG 56, and South Country ones in Gillington's *Eight Hampshire Folk Songs* (1907) and Carey's *Ten English Folk Songs* (1915). FSJ I (1) 1899 21 has a Sussex set from Mr Copper of Rottingdean. Versions from Devon, Kent and Essex (four examples [tunes only]) are in FSJ IV (15) 1910 124-6. In JEFDSS VII (2) 1953 151 is a version recorded in 1952 in the 'home-made' harmonies of the Copper family. In the 1930s, Phillip Tanner of Gower, South Wales, recorded the song on a commercial gramophone record (Columbia FB 1570, later re-issued as RO 101). Tune and text have shown remarkable constancy through these several versions. Clearly, singers have found the song unusually memorable and satisfactory, for the process of oral transmission seems to have worked little change on it.

[Phil Tanner's version can be heard on Topic Records TSCD 651, *Come Let Us Buy the Licence*. See also DPG 6; ED&S 28 (2) 1966 45 (a version from Baring-Gould's MSS); PCL 5; PECC 141; SLM 8, and SYB I 3-4. The Copper family have recorded their set a number of times; it is currently available on *Come Write Me Down: Early Recordings of the Copper Family of Rottingdean* (Topic TSCD534, 2001); *Coppersongs 2* (Coppersongs CD2, 1995), and in CSB 9 and CSES (1971) 218-9 (1997) 155-6. A version sung by Fred Jordan of Shropshire appears on *A Century of Song*. A number of nineteenth century broadside examples can be seen at the Bodleian Library website. The song was evidently a great favourite, and more common than its representation in song collections might suggest; primroses, Henry Hammond remarked, 'were so numerous we did not stop to gather any'.]

The Basket of Eggs

(FSJ II (7) 1905 102) Roud 377

This wry song of two sailors who thought to outwit a trusting girl and were themselves tricked, has been found in slightly differing versions in districts as far apart as Norfolk (FSJ I (2) 1900 46 and II (7) 1905 103) and Herefordshire (FSJ II (7) 1905 102), Sussex (FSJ II (7) 1905 102) and Shetland (JEFDSS VI (1) 1949 16). It is sometimes confused with *The Oyster Girl* [Roud 875 Laws Q13], a song that gained wide currency in the nineteenth century through its use by popular stage comedians. However, the two songs seem to be separate.

[Roy Palmer, PRVW 130, mentions a version appearing as *Eggs and Bacon* in a chapbook of 1796, *The Man of War's Garland*. See also FMJ 2 (4) 1973 284 for a set from George Dunn of Staffordshire, which can also be heard on Musical Traditions MTCD317-8, *George Dunn: Chainmaker*. Other sets appear in SLM 32, PRVW 130-1: REC 99-100; RIP 73, and PCL 27-8. For a broadside edition, see Bodleian, Harding B 28(166).]

Benjamin Bowmaneer

(JEFDSS I (2) 1933 97) Roud 1514

In folklore, the poor tailor seldom plays a noble part, perhaps because his profession does not call for lustihood. 'Nine tailors make a man', says the proverb, and a popular children's rhyme tells of four and twenty tailors frightened by a snail [ODNR no. 496]. The amusing Benjamin Bowmaneer seems to perpetuate the folks' injustice to men of an honourable trade. Perhaps the song has a secondary, satirical meaning that eludes us? It has been suggested that 'Castors away' may mean 'Hats off', the castor being a slang word for a beaver hat, or by extension, any headgear. It may also mean 'Cast us away!', and thus be related to a sailors' song. The tune's resemblance to the *Spanish Ladies* melody, much used for sea-song texts, would seem to strengthen this possibility. We have not found a set of this song complete with tune elsewhere.

[Mary E. Spence of Patterdale learned the song (via her father and sister) from her great-aunt, Sarah Foster of Sedburgh, who had it from a travelling tailor who came to mend her father's clothes somewhere between 1804 and 1807. Only one verse appeared in the *Journal*, the editor commenting, 'The words follow the well-known version and are not here reprinted.' Eighty years on, it is no longer clear to whom the words may have been well-known apart from Mr Howes, from whom the editors presumably obtained the full text; although Mary Spence's original letter survives (Vaughan Williams Memorial Library, Gilchrist Collection AGG/10/340), she had requested that her song notation be returned to her once it had been copied for the *Journal*.

A set found in America appeared in *Western Folklore* (II (3) 1952 175), and one recorded by James M. Carpenter from Sam Bennett of Ilmington, Warwickshire, was printed in PBB 122-3. There is an unpublished version from the USA (music and one verse) in Cecil Sharp's MSS, and another, *Benjamin Bowlabags*, in Baring-Gould's MSS, where the louse featured in most versions has become a mouse. The louse has long been associated with tailors, and the related song *The Tailor and the Louse* (Roud 16577; see FSJ VIII (34) 1930 213-4) also features a formal funeral for a deceased insect. In that example the louse is a personal friend and dies of natural causes, but the song's broadside ancestor, *A Bloody Battle between a Taylor and a Louse*, and the earlier mock-heroic piece sometimes attributed (probably in error) to John Taylor, the Water-Poet, *A dreadful Battle between a Taylor and a Louse* (c.1655, later re-issued as *The War-Like Taylor*) do have a combat sequence.]

The Blacksmith

(FSJ VIII (34) 1930 208) Roud 816

The faithful 'hero' of this song is just as often a shoemaker as a blacksmith. Both metre and tune are rather unusual, recalling the well-known *Brisk Young Widow* [Roud 2438] in SFS III, and *Brave Wolfe* [Roud 961 Laws A1], a song celebrating the hero of Quebec, often found in America though not reported in Britain (*Brave Wolfe* is not to be confused with *Bold General Wolfe* [Roud 624], which is fairly common in England). The opening of the 'strange news' verse also appears in some sets of *Brave Wolfe*. *The Blacksmith* (or *Shoemaker*) has been reported from Sussex (FSJ IV (17) 1913 279), Essex (FSJ IV, (17) 1913 280 – two versions), Somerset (FSJ VIII (31) 1927 17) and Dorset (FSJ VIII (34) 1930 206).

[Mrs Powell's tune appeared in the *Journal* without words, RVW having noted none from her. The text here was supplied by him from an unspecified source; Roy Palmer (PRVW 76) suggests that it may have been adapted from a broadside printed by Such; for which, see Bodleian, Firth c.18(130). The most likely candidate, though, seems to be the Sussex set mentioned, noted by Butterworth from Peter Verrall, which, though incomplete, is very close; with perhaps some modifications from the Somerset version, noted by Sharp from William Chorley, and from the broadside. The 'good black billycock' has so far proved elusive. Mrs Powell had at least one verse, which was communicated to RVW by Ella M. Leather, who also noted songs from her:

A blacksmith courted me, both late and early.
A blacksmith courted me, I loved him dearly:
With his hammer in his hand, striking a fire,
I'll go to my true love, that is my desire.

(Vaughan Williams Scrapbook p. 57). See also KFBI 346 and PRVW 76-7.]

The Bold Benjamin

(FSJ III (11) 1907 93) Roud 2632

The singer learned this song from a man-o'-war's man in the 1850s. We know no details of the unlucky expedition it celebrates. The song is a latter-day re-make of a black-letter ballad, published *c.*1670, called *The Benjamin's Lamentation for their Sad Loss at Sea, by Storms and Tempests.* (Roxburghe Ballads, VII 529), beginning 'Captain Chilver's gone to sea, I, boys, O boys!' C. H. Firth, in *Naval Songs and Ballads* (Navy Records Society, 1908) remarks on the interesting metrical form of *The Benjamin's Lamentation*, and suggests that it may be an early shanty. [For two examples of the older broadside, see Bodleian, Don. b.13(5) and Douce Ballads 1(16a). It is also reprinted in PBC 58.]

The Bramble Briar

(FSJ V (19) 1915 123) Roud 18 Laws M32

This interesting ballad, not included in the Child compilation, is based on a story that was probably not new when Boccaccio made it famous in the fourteenth century [*Decameron* IV 5]. Hans Sachs put it into verse some two hundred years later [*Der ermordete Lorenz*], and in the nineteenth century, Keats rewrote it as *Isabella and the Pot of Basil*. The English traditional versions are quite unlike Keats's, but are very close to Hans Sachs's rendering. Besides this Hertfordshire version, sets of the ballad have been reported in print from Somerset (FSJ II (6) 1905 42; V (19) 1915 126) and Hampshire (GOR 10). Mrs Joiner was unable to remember clearly the beginning of the ballad, and our first two stanzas are from the version obtained by Cecil Sharp from Mrs Overd of Langport, Somerset, in 1904.

[Mrs Joiner's song appeared in the *Journal* as *Lord Burling's* (or *Burlington's*) *Sister*; or, *The Murdered Servant-Man*; she herself had no title for it. Versions have been found quite widely in England and (particularly) the USA, under a great many names from *Bruton*, *Strawberry*, or *Seaport Town* to *The Bamboo Brier*. See also ED&S 37 (1) 1975 20; PECS 111-3; PWS 79-80; REC 105-6, and S100 4-5 (collated). It does not seem to have been printed on broadsides, but a nineteenth century broadside song which may derive from it, *The Merchant's Daughter and Constant Farmer's Son* (Roud 675 Laws M33), is also found in tradition. See, among several editions of the latter, Bodleian, Johnson Ballads 1223, which credits authorship to a G[eorge] Brown (to whom *Flora, the Lily of the West* (Roud 957 Laws P29) and *The Bonny Bunch of Roses* (Roud 664 Laws J5) are also sometimes attributed) and specifies the tune of *Young Edwin in the Lowlands*.]

The Broomfield Hill

(FSJ IV (15) 1910 114) Roud 34 Child 43

This ancient ballad was a great favourite with singers in England and Scotland. Sharp alone collected at least twelve distinct versions. It was often printed on broadsheets and in America a good version found its way into a popular pocket song book, *The Pearl Songster*, about the middle of the nineteenth century. Some texts make it clear that the bold girl had bewitched the lover into his deep sleep. In England, other versions of the song have been reported from Dorset (FSJ III (11) 1917 69, IV (15) 1910 115, VII (27) 1923 31), Lincolnshire (FSJ IV (15) 1910 110), Somerset (FSJ IV (15) 1910 112, VII (27) 1923 33), Norfolk, Hereford (both FSJ IV (15) 1910 114) and Essex (FSJ VIII (33) 1929 127).

[Further examples appear in JEFDSS 9 (4) 1963 187-8; ED&S 29 (3) 1967 82; DPG 29; PECS 121-3; PFD 11; PRVW 40-1, and SMFL 4-5. *The Pearl Songster* was published by C. P. Huestis, New York, 1846. For broadside examples, see, among others: Bodleian, Douce Ballads 2(153a): *The Merry Broomfield* or, *The West Country Wager*, Tho. Norris [London] between 1711 and 1732; and Firth

c.21(14): *The Merry Broom Fields: or, The West Country Wager*, Such [London] between 1863 and 1885. The song persists in tradition to the present day. See also Child I 390-99 and Bronson I 336-347.]

The Cock-Fight (The Bonny Grey)

(FSJ II (7) 1905 84) Roud 211

It is generally agreed that the weight and blackness of the Industrial Revolution took the heart out of most of our folk-singers. Yet some fine songs lingered on in industrial towns, and balladeers who made songs for Lancashire spinners and Yorkshire weavers and Cumberland and Durham miners were still at work late in the nineteenth century. They no longer sang of the clash of bright swords. Rather they preferred to take the popular newspaper themes — murder, adultery, prize-fighting, sometimes horse-racing. Long after cockfighting was made illegal, the cruel sport and its lively ballad persisted on the northern moors and fells. Various versions place the cockfight at Walney Island in Westmorland, at Holbeck Moor and Hunslet in Yorkshire, and in Liverpool. All agree that after a hard fight the Bonny Grey was the victor.

The text, sung to Cecil Sharp by Mr Collinson at the Kendal folk song competition in 1905, is amended and clarified from a Yorkshire version in KTT [pp. 135-7; verse 5, lines 3 and 4 here], another in A. L. Lloyd's *Come All ye Bold Miners* [revised edition, 1978, pp. 88-9; verse 5, lines 1 and 2 and verse 6, line 1 here], and from a broadsheet printed by Harkness of Preston [verse 3, altered].

[The editors have also made various textual modifications of their own, and softened the dialect. Two of Mr Collinson's verses were removed altogether:

(After our verse 1)
When these two cocks com' to be shown,
The north Sceeal shouts w'll fight none;
Reasons why they all did say,
The charcoal black's t' big for the gray.

(After our verse 5)
Now this black cock he hes lost
Which med Biggar lads to swear an' corss
They wished they'd nivver cum that day
T' Tumler's hill t' see the play.

Mr Collinson's full text appears in PECS 204-5. For the Harkness broadside, see Bodleian, Harding B 11(408). See also CPM 11 659-60, *The Hathersage Cocking*.]

The Cruel Mother

(FSJ III (2) 1907 71) Roud 9 Child 20

The great Scottish collector Gavin Greig believed that 'the numerous versions of this ballad are practically all Scottish', but in fact it has been widespread in England too, a form of it even turning up as a London children's street game (N. Douglas, *London Street Games*, 1931 ed., 47; [also Iona and Peter Opie, *The Lore and Language of Schoolchildren*, 1959, 33]). Apart from that version, and our Essex set, the ballad has been reported from oral tradition in Gloucestershire (WUP 295), Shropshire (BSFL 540), Dorset (FSJ III (2) 1907 70-72), Somerset (SFS IV 54 [and S100 35, text completed from other sources]), and (again as a game song) in Lancashire (FSJ VI (22) 1919 80).

[Further examples are in JEFDSS 7 (2) 1953 101 (Cecilia Costello), PMB 22,

and SLM 30. The Shropshire set referred to above is reprinted in PBB 54-5. Beside Scotland and England, versions have also been found in Ireland (where it also occurs sometimes as a children's song), and widely in the USA and Canada. A broadside of *c*.1690, *The Duke's Daughter's Cruelty: Or the Wonderful Apparition of two Infants whom she Murther'd and Buried in a Forrest, for to hide her Shame*, was reproduced in FMJ 6 (3) 1992 361, in David Atkinson's article *History, Symbol and Meaning in 'The Cruel Mother'*. See also *The Duke's Daughter's Cruelty*, ED&S 64 (3) 2002 15.

Only one verse of Mrs Bowring's set was published in the Journal:

'Oh! babes, oh! babes, if you were mine,
All alone and aloney,
I would dress you in scarlet fine.'
Down by the greenwood sidey.

The editors have set to Mrs Bowring's tune the entire text noted by Clive Carey (1911) and George Chambers (1921) from Mrs Hollingsworth of Sibley's Green, Thaxted, Essex, which appeared in JEFDSS I (3) 1934 130. Her melody was very different; Anne Gilchrist noted a resemblance to the Northern dance-tune *Iron Legs*. See also Child I 218-227 and Bronson I 276-296.]

The Daughter of Peggy, O

(FSJ V (20) 1916 260) Roud 117 Child 277

The cautionary tale of the shrew tamed by flogging seems to have been common in bygone days, first as a serious homily, later as comedy. It has given rise to many songs, including *The Wife Wrapt in Wether's Skin*, the well-known *Wee Cooper o' Fife*

[FSJ II (9) 1906 223; PBB 213-3], *Ruggleton's Daughter of Iero* (SFS IV 52 and S100 158), the nursery ballad *Robin-a-Thrush* (BGS 102[, FSJ II (9) 1906 225, PFD 78]) [all classified as Roud 117, Child 277] and *On Monday Morning* ([Roud 433, Laws Q6] p.000 in this present collection).

[The editors have partly re-written the text, apparently with reference to a version noted by Sharp from Miss Gooding at Somerton, Somerset, in 1907 (SFS IV 52 and KCSC I 196). Examples of this song group have been found very widely, and it is still current in tradition. Child (V 104) cites a London broadside ballad of the later sixteenth century, *A merry jeste of a shrewde and curste wyfe lapped in Morrelles skin for her good behauyour*, as perhaps ancestral to the group. See also Child V 104-106 and Bronson IV 143-173.]

Death and the Lady

(JEFDSS V (1) 1946 19) Roud 1031

In the Middle Ages, the Dance of Death and dialogues between Death and his victims used to be enacted as a stage morality. Later, the theme was taken up by artists as great as Holbein and as humble as the chapbook illustrators. Miss Anne Gilchrist has noted (JEFDSS IV (2) 1941 37-48) that 'in English balladry the favourite aspect of the subject was Death in its relation to radiant beauty and lusty and careless youth.' The ballad, perhaps of late sixteenth century origin, was originally in dialogue-form and it may well have been at once sung and acted. Traditional versions have been noted from Devon (BGSW 202-3), Somerset (SFS IV 4 [also S100 52-4 and KCSC I 233-4]), Wiltshire (WUP 173) and Sussex (BTSC 40 [and FSJ I (4) 1902 169]).

[Verses 1-3 and 6 appeared in the *Journal*. Verses 4 and 5 are from elsewhere; probably adapted from WUP. See also FSJ II (7) 1905 137-8; PCL 20, and *Still Growing* 78. The earliest extant broadside edition seems to be *The great messenger of mortality: or, A dialogue betwixt Death and a beautiful lady*, published by J. Deacon between 1685 and 1689 (Bodleian, Wood 417(129); no image is available online at the time of writing) though this may have been based on an earlier piece. A tune 'stolen from an old ballad called *Death and the Lady*' appeared in Henry Carey's *Musical Century* (1738) and in two ballad operas of 1729 and 1730. It is quoted in FSJ II (7) 1905 138. See also, among other later editions, Bodleian, Harding B 2(17): *Death and the lady; or, The great messenger of mortality*; Harding B 11(828): *Death and the lady*; Douce Ballads 4(46): *Messenger of mortality, or Life and Death contrasted*.]

The Death of Queen Jane

(FSJ III (11) 1907 67) Roud 77 Child 170

The story is a legendary re-working of historical fact. Jane Seymour, wife of Henry VIII, died on 24 October, 1537, twelve days after the natural birth of her son, who later became Edward VI. Some said her death was due to clumsy surgery. We do not know how old this ballad is, nor if it derives from a piece called *The Lamentation of Queen Jane*, licensed for publication in 1560. The ballad has been collected in Devon (FSJ II (9) 1906 222) and Somerset (FSJ V (20) 1916 257-8), and a second Dorset version is given in

FSJ III (11) 67. *The Death of Queen Jane* is No. 170 in Child's collection.

[Only verses 1-6 as given here came from Mrs Russell. The editors have modified verse 3 from the third set mentioned above, and added the final three verses – a little altered – from the Somerset version in FSJ V, noted by Sharp from Mrs Eliza Sweet at Somerton, 1906 (see also *Still Growing* 88 and S100 68-9). Further versions appear in FSJ II (9) 1906 221-2; Child III 372-6, and Bronson III 144-150. For a broadside edition of *c.*1820, see Bodleian, Harding B 16(71c).]

The Deserter from Kent

(FSJ V (19) 1915 154-5) Roud 2510

Most of the songs about army deserters current in England have the ring of street balladry rather than of country tradition. Many appear to have been made by Irishmen. The present song would seem to be an exception. Two missing lines [3 and 4] in the penultimate verse have been restored from the related Army song: *The Rambling Royal* [Roud 982, Laws J15]. The text of *The Deserter from Kent* is rare, and only this version has appeared in print. The tune, however, is a variant of the familiar 'Villikins' air, perhaps the commonest of all British folk-melodies.

[The editors have slightly re-written the final verse. A further version subsequently appeared in Ewan MacColl and Peggy Seeger, *Travellers' Songs from England and Scotland*, 274-5. For versions of *The Rambling Royal*, see PBB 123-4, and Bodleian, 2806 c.15(252) and 2806 c.18(24): *Belfast Shoe Maker*.]

The Devil and the Ploughman

(FSJ II (8) 1906 184) Roud 160 Child 278

The Devil comes to fetch a farmer's wife. The farmer is delighted. But the shrewish woman behaves so abominably in Hell that the Devil is obliged to bring her back again. The song, apparently common all over the British Isles and frequently recorded in America, seems to embody a very old joke indeed. Perhaps in early forms, the farmer had enlisted the Devil's aid with his ploughing, promising the soul of one of his family in return. Most versions of this song have a whistled refrain, and this is not without sly meaning, for there is an old belief that whistling summons the Devil (hence the sailors' superstition that whistling aboard ship may bring on a storm). Burns remade a Scottish version of the ballad, and called it *The Carle o' Killyburn Braes*. Mrs Burns, speaking to a scholar [Robert Cromek] of the way in which her husband altered folk songs, remarked: 'Robert gae this ane a terrible brushing.' Our text is filled out with some verses obtained by Alfred Williams from David Sawyer, of Ogbourne, Wiltshire (WUP 211). A Dorset version is given in FSJ III (11) 1907 131-2.

[Verses 1, 5, 6, 7, 9 and 10 here are from WUP, in some cases a little altered with reference to equivalent verses in Mr Burstow's (eight stanza) version. Some of his remaining verses have also been 'brushed'. Our heroine's arrival in Hell is even more undignified as he had it:

The devil he took her upon his prong,
And into hell he put her headlong.

Two versions noted by Seamus Ennis in Northern Ireland appear in JEFDSS VIII

(1) 1956 27-8. See also ED&S 47 (2) 1985 14; PBB 214-5; PMB 24; Child V 107-8 and Bronson IV 174-212. The broadside *A Pleasant new Ballad you here may behold, How the Devill, though subtle, was gull'd by a Scold* was registered in 1630. For a later edition, see Bodleian, 4o Rawl. 566(169); also Harding B 11(879): *The Devil in Search of a Wife*; and Harding B 25(1855): *The Sussex Farmer*.]

Droylsden Wakes

(FSJ V (19) 1915 204) Roud 3290

This Lancashire dialogue song was once associated with a folk ceremonial attached to the local 'wakes' or annual holiday. The custom was for two men in comic dress, one of them travestied as a woman, to sit in a cart with a spinning-wheel before them, spinning flax as they sang the song, and collecting money from onlookers. The ceremonial may go back to ancient times, though it does not seem to have reached Droylsden until early in the nineteenth century. The tune is of the primitive sort often used for wassails, May Day songs and other festive ceremonial purposes. There is some doubt whether the refrain means 'Tread the wheel' or 'Thread ye well'. A description of the ceremonial, with a text of the song, is in John Harland's *Ballads and Songs of Lancashire* (1865).

[The editors have regularised the spelling a little. In 1907, Anne Gilchrist wrote to the 'Notes and Queries' column of the *Manchester City News* to appeal for information about Morris dance tunes and related customs, and Mr Bates was one of those who replied with memories of the Wakes, the rush carts and the Morris dancers. He had first heard the song

around 1844, but did not remember all the words, and referred Miss Gilchrist to Higson's *History of Droylsden*, 1859, for the rest. She visited him in the summer of 1908 to note the tune (Gilchrist Collection, AGG/4/50 and AGG/4/49). There are three further verses, quoted here from John Harland and T. T. Wilkinson, *Ballads and Songs of Lancashire* (2nd edition, 1875, 147-50):

He:
Com, com, mi dear woife, aw'll not ha' thè rue,
Un this aw will tell yo, an aw'll tell yo true,
Neaw if yo'll forgie me for what aw have said,
Aw'll do my endavur to pleos yo' instead.

She:
Aw'm glad for to yeor 'ot yo win me forgive,
Un' aw will do by yo os lung os aw live;
So let us unite, un' live free fro' o' sin,
Un' then we shall have nowt to think on but spin.

Both:
So now let's conclude, and here undeth eawr sung,
Aw hope it has pleost this numerous throng;
Bur iv it 'os mist, yo needn't to fear,
We'll do eawr endavur to pleos yo next year.

The custom seems to have been brought to Droylsden around 1814 from Woodhouses, near Failsworth, where it had a prior history of more than thirty years. Originally, the couple rode on horseback, but one year the 'husband' got drunk and fell off his horse in the yard of Cinderland Hall; the cart was introduced in order to avoid further accidents. The song was known locally as *Threedewell* or *Threedy-Wheel*. A polished-up text appears in Robert Bell's *Songs of the Peasantry*, 1857, as *The Greenside Wakes Song*; Greenside being the part of Droylsden from which the procession started out. Harland quotes some further verse-fragments, including

The tow that aw spin is five shilling a peawnd,
Un that yo mun kneaw by mi wheel going reawnd

and

Theaw cankert owd besom, aw conno' endure
Ony lunger a temper loike thoine is, aw'm sure.]

The False Bride

(FSJ II (6) 1905 14) Roud 154

This tender melancholy song has remained long in the affection of country singers. Its age is uncertain. A version of the ballad was published in Newcastle late in the seventeenth century, but it may not have been new then. It is still to be found among folk singers in the South of England. Some call it *The Week Before Easter*, and sing the first verse:

The week before Easter, the morn bright and clear,
The sun it shone brightly, and keen blowed the air,
I went up in the forest for to gather fine flowers,
But the forest won't yield me no roses.

Mrs White's text has been slightly amended with lines from two other Somerset versions collected by Cecil Sharp in 1904 [from Mrs Emma Overd and Mrs Elizabeth Mogg] (FSJ II (6) 1905 12-13). Other versions have been printed from Devon (BGSW 198) and Sussex (FSJ I (1) 1899 23).

[Mrs White learned this song at Weston-super-Mare. Also found in tradition in Scotland, Ireland and Canada. Further versions appear in JEFDSS IV (5) 1944 185-6; CSB 1 and CSES (1971) 236-7 (1997) 175-6; KFBI 352; PFD 28; PECS 152-3, and SYB I 27-8. Lucy White's sister, Louie Hooper, was recorded singing it by the BBC in 1942 (BBC recording 4039). For broadside editions, see Bodleian, Douce Ballads 1(83a): *The Forlorn Lover: declaring how a lass gave her love three slips for a teaster, and married another a week before Easter* (London, between 1663 and 1674); Douce Ballads 3(32a) n.d.; and Harding B 11(634): *The false hearted lover* (Birmingham, c.1850).]

Fare Thee Well, my Dearest Dear

(FSJ II (8) 1906 201) Roud 1035

[No notes were given for this song, which the editors have 'tidied up' a little. It does not appear to have been found elsewhere in tradition, but is descended from a broadside song of the later seventeenth century, *The Two Faithful Lovers*. An edition printed between 1663 and 1674 for F. Coles, T. Vere, and J. Wright (London) can be seen in the Bodleian collection: Douce Ballads 2(213b). See also Douce Ballads 2(223b) and Don. b.13(30). The tune prescribed was *Franklin is Fled Away*, and this is ancestral to Mrs Verrall's melody (see Simpson, *The British Broadside Ballad and Its Music*, pp. 232-5).]

The Gaol Song

(FSJ VII (27) 1923 47-8) Roud 1077

English tradition includes many crime songs but relatively few dealing with life in prison. The broadside ballads of Bellevue, Wakefield, and Kirkdale gaols, published by Bebbington of Manchester and Harkness of Preston, all derive from the same 'original', issued several times in London by the Catnach Press and its successors as *The County Gaol*. A different ballad, called *Durham Gaol*, said to be the work of the pitman-balladeer Thomas Armstrong, was current on Tyneside till recently (see A. L. Lloyd: *Come All ye Bold Miners*, [revised edition, 1978, 324-5]). Each of these bears some relation to our *Gaol Song*, of which two versions, with separate melodies, were collected by H. E. D. Hammond in Beaminster, Dorset, in June 1906.

[William Davey's text has been modified, and verses 1, 2 and 4 introduced, from the other version, noted from Sam Gregory at Beaminster, 1906 (FSJ VII (27) 1923 48-9). Mr Davey (or Davy) had another verse:

At ten o'clock our doctor comes round
With a pen and paper in his hand;
If we say we are not ill
So all next day to the treading mill.

The editors have made some further changes, including substituting 'Our hobnail boots and tin mugs too' for 'Our jackboots and our goglets too' and 'the jangle rings' for 'our bell did ring'. For editions of the prison broadsides mentioned, see Bodleian, Harding B 11(233) (*Bellevue Goal* [sic]); Firth c.26(19), Firth c.17(73) (*A new song on Wakefield gaol*) and Harding B 11(3501) (*Wakefield jail, or, Face the wall*); Harding B 11(2000) and 2806 c.16(63) (*Kirkdale Gaol*); Firth b.26(213) (*County Gaol*); Harding B 25(565) (*Durham gaol. A new song*).]

The Gentleman Soldier

(FSJ V (19) 1915 156) Roud 178

This jaunty song, common in the army and quoted by Kipling in *Soldiers Three*, has rarely found its way into the conventional song collections. The text, printed in incomplete form in the *Folk Song Journal*, is amplified from a Somerset version collected by H. E. D. Hammond and not hitherto published. The melody is a military-sounding version of the widespread tune called *Drumdelgie* in Scotland and *Dydd Llun y Boreu* in Wales.

[Verses 1 and 3 here, together with the chorus and the first half of verse 5, appeared in the *Journal*; they have been modified slightly, with reference to broadsides and to the set noted from Mrs Gulliver of Combe Florey, Somerset (Hammond MS Sm. 51), from whom the other material also comes. Four of her five verses were later published in PCL 88, together with one verse and tune noted by George Gardiner from Richard Laney, Axford, Hampshire. Mr Coomber, who had apparently been in the local militia and had learned the song in camp, had another verse and a half, equivalent to our verses 4 and 5 (Gilchrist Collection AGG/8/27), but they were a little muddled and were not printed in the *Journal*. Frank Kidson noted that a 'gentleman soldier' was one in a yeomanry regiment. For broadside editions, see Bodleian, Harding B 11(3449); Firth c.14(203), and Harding B 12(162): *The Sentry Box*, and Harding B

11(3013): *The gentleman soldier*. The poet John Clare knew it as a fiddle tune, *The Soldier's Cloak*, and Roy Palmer prints it from the Clare MS tunebook, with a broadside text, in *The Rambling Soldier* (Penguin Books, 1977 134-5). See also George Deacon, *John Clare and the Folk Tradition* (London: Sinclair Browne, 1983 366).]

Geordie

(FSJ IV (17) 1913 333) Roud 90 Child 209

This ballad is well-known both in England and Scotland. The Scottish sets differ considerably from the English ones, for in them the hero is not a thief but a nobleman, thought by some scholars to be George Gordon, Earl of Huntly, who suffered royal displeasure when he showed clemency towards a Highland robber in 1554. In the English versions, which may be re-makes of the Scottish, the main character is always an outlaw. An old black-letter ballad names him as George Stoole of Northumberland, who was executed in 1610; but even in its 'robber' form (if that is the more recent) the song probably pre-dates the seventeenth century. Mr Neville's tune is related to the well-known air of *Searching for Lambs*. *Geordie* has been found in oral tradition also in Sussex (FSJ I (4) 1902 164 and II (8) 1906 208), Cambridgeshire (VWE 47-9), Somerset (FSJ II (6) 1905 27-8 and IV (17) 1913 333), Norfolk (FSJ IV (15) 1910 89-90), Suffolk, Surrey and Dorset (FSJ IV (17) 1913 332-3) and Yorkshire (KTT 24-26).

[Only Mr Neville's tune appeared in the *Journal*. The bulk of the text here is from the set noted by Sharp from Mrs Overd (FSJ II (6) 1905 27 and S100 24-5), mixed with material from Mr W. Debbidge (RVW and Ivor Gatty, FSJ IV (15) 1910 89-90) and other sources. Further versions appeared in FSJ III (1908) 191-2 (Joseph Taylor, Lincolnshire, tune only); JEFDSS VIII (3) 1958 148-9 (Harry Cox, Norfolk); FMJ 3 (1) 1975 73-4 (Levi Smith, Surrey); ED&S 42 (3) 1980 17-18, and PECS 83-5. See also Child IV 123-142 and Bronson III 268-289. The black-letter ballad referred to, *A lamentable new ditty, made upon the death of a worthy gentleman named George Stoole, dwelling sometime on Gate-side Moore, and sometime at New-Castle in Northumberland: with his penitent end*, is quoted, with another related broadside of the late seventeenth century, *The Life and Death of George of Oxford*, in Child IV 140-142. Both contain elements found in traditional English and American forms of the song. For nineteenth century broadside editions, see Bodleian, Harding B 11(1797): *The life of Georgey*; Harding B 25(488): *Death of Georgy*; Harding B 11(2297): *Maid's lamentation for her Georgy*; and Harding B 16(137b): *Maiden's lamentation for her Georgy*.]

George Collins

(FSJ III (13) 1909 301) Roud 147 Child 42/85

A man meets a girl by a stream; he kisses her; he returns home and dies; at the sight of his coffin, his true-love realizes the tragedy and prepares to die in turn. The plot of *George Collins* has its secrets. From an examination of a number of variants, the full story becomes clearer. The girl by the stream is a water-fairy. The young man has been in the habit of visiting her. He is about to marry a mortal, and the fairy takes her revenge with a poisoned kiss. The song telling that story is among the great ballads of Europe. Its roots and branches are spread in Scandinavia, Germany, France, Italy, Spain and elsewhere. An early literary form is the German poem of the Knight of Staufenberg (c. 1310). France alone has about ninety versions, mostly in the form of the familiar *Renaud*, though here much of the dream-quality of the tale is missing, since the girl by the stream is lost sight of, and instead the hero is mortally wounded in battle. The first half of the *George Collins* story is told in the ballad called *Clerk Colvill* (Child 42), the second half in *Lady Alice* (Child 85). Either these are two separate songs which have been combined to form *George Collins* or (which seems more likely) they are two fragments of the completer ballad. *George Collins* has rarely been reported in England, though in the summer of 1906 Dr G. B. Gardiner collected three separate versions in different Hampshire villages (two of them on the same day) (FSJ III (13) 1909 299-301).

[Only the first verse and tune here were quoted in the *Journal* from Mr Stansbridge. The editors have constructed the rest of the text from two other sets also given, noted from Henry Gaylor and Philip Gaylor, both at Minstead, New Forest, Hampshire, 1906. The song has been found quite widely in tradition in the USA and has been reported in England at least as recently as the 1970s. Gardiner found six sets in Hampshire, and a version collated from five of them is printed in PWS 46-7. A set recorded by Bob Copper from Enos White of Hampshire appears in JEFDSS IX (2) 1961 72-3, and can be heard on Topic Records, *O'er his Grave the Grass Grew*

Green (TSCD 653 1998). See also Child I 371-89 and II 279-80, and Bronson I 334-5 and II 392-407. For a discussion of the ballad and its antecedents by Barbara M. Cra'ster, see FSJ IV (15) 1910 106-9.]

The Golden Vanity

(FSJ II (9) 1906 244) Roud 122 Child 286

In some versions of this favourite ballad, the enemy is Turkish; in others, he is Spanish or French. Rarely, the song has a happy ending, with the boy saved and rewarded. Occasionally it concludes with the boy drowned, and his ghost returning to sink his own ship. More usually it ends as here, with the boy rejected by the cruel captain and pulled aboard too late by his shipmates. Samuel Pepys preserved a seventeenth-century broadside version in which the hero was Sir Walter Raleigh, but later singers seem to have cast aside this detail. The melody given here is quite different from that usually taught in schools. The text comes in the main from the version collected in 1900 by W. P. Merrick from Henry Hills, at Shepperton, Middlesex (FSJ I (3) 1901 104-5). Mr Bolton explained that the 'black bear skin' was the cabin boy's covering at night, and that he wished to wear it as a disguise in the water. Other versions have been reported from Wiltshire (WUP 199-200) and Cornwall (BGSW 136-7).

[Only verse 4 here is from Mr Bolton. The editors have re-written the additional material to conform to his pattern. See also JEFDSS 9 (3) 1962 165-166 (Tristan da Cunha); HGG 78-79 (Cambridgeshire); PCL 37-38 (Hampshire); PBB 108 (Sussex); S100 36-7; SMFL 12-13; Child V 135-142, and

Bronson IV 312-362. The Pepys broadside is Child's example 286A; for a nineteenth century edition by Such, see Bodleian, Harding B 11(1086). The ballad has been particularly widespread in tradition in the USA.]

The Green Bed

(FSJ III (13) 1909 281-2) Roud 276 Laws K36

During the nineteenth century the ballad press issued a large number of broadsides setting out the sailor's disgust with the treatment received at the hands of grasping landladies and their faithless daughters. That many of these songs resemble each other seems to be the result of influence rather than accident. *Green Beds*, 'a song popular both in the foc'sle and in the cottage', tells the tale in fullest detail and must be regarded as the most important ballad on this theme. A fairly close relative is the well-known song, *The Wild Rover* [Roud 1173]. *The Green Bed* has also been collected in Warwickshire (FSJ I (2) 1900 48), Somerset (FSJ V (18) 1914 68) and Devon (BGSW 186-7, with words re-written).

[The editors have re-constructed lines missing from Mr Arnold's text, and the whole of verses 3 and 5, from the Warwickshire set mentioned, from a version noted by RVW from an unnamed singer in the workhouse at Barnard Castle, Co. Durham, in 1911 (RVW MS 8vo B 15), and from broadside editions; for which, see, among others, Bodleian, Harding B 11(1848): *Jack Tar, or The green bed empty*; Harding B 11(2178): *Liverpool landlady*, and Harding B 25(1353): *A New Song*. They have also added a few small touches of their own. The Durham set is quoted (amended) in PRVW 22. See also

PWS 48-9 (Hampshire) and DPG 40-1 (Norfolk). A 'green bed' was a temporary one, typically made up with a mattress stuffed with greenery.]

The Greenland Whale Fishery

(FSJ II (9) 1906 243) Roud 347 Laws K21

Until 1830, the whaling ships put out each spring from London, King's Lynn, Hull, Whitby, bound for the right-whale grounds of Greenland. The best of our whaling ballads are about the Greenland fishery. After 1830, the fleets moved to Baffin's Bay, and subsequently to the grounds off Hawaii and Peru, but still most of the songs the whalermen sang were of the Greenland days. The present song is quite old, a form of it being published as a black-letter ballad before 1725. It was evidently popular in the nineteenth century, since Pitts, Such, and Catnach each issued broadside versions, giving 1824 as the date of the incident described. Sharp published a version in which the date is 1861 – thirty years too late for Greenland whaling. This adventurous song is still to be met with among traditional singers. This text comes partly from the broadsides by Catnach and Such. The song is also reported from Somerset (SFS III 54) and Norfolk (FSJ VIII (35) 1931 279), while Baring-Gould (BGG 56) and Whall (WSS 69) have unlocated versions giving the date as 1794. The singer consistently sang an F sharp in the concluding phrase, though the tune has a strongly mixolydian character.

[Mr Bolton remembered only one verse, the last given here (modified):

Oh, Greenland is a cold country,
A land where grows no tree,

92

Where the ice and the snow and the whale-fish blow,
And the daylight's seldom seen, brave boys,
And the daylight's seldom seen.

See Bodleian, Harding B 11(3307A): *Whale Fishery* (Catnach); Harding B 11(2057): *GreenlandWhale Fishery* (Such); Harding B 28(284): *The Whale Fishing*; Harding B 11(1420) and 2806 c.17(159): *Greenland Fishery*, and other examples. The early ballad referred to was *The Greenland Voyage; or, the Whale-Fisher's Delight*, printed in *A Collection of Old Ballads*, III 1725 172; Baring-Gould (BGG 57) points out that the metre and the incidents described are quite different from those we have here. Harry Cox's Norfolk set (FSJ VIII) is also printed in PBC 170-1. See also PFD 37 (Hampshire).]

The Grey Cock or The Lover's Ghost

(JEFDSS VII (2) 1953 97) Roud 179 Child 248

A number of lyrical folk songs present the situation of two lovers disturbed by the early crowing of a cock. Perhaps the origin of these songs is found in this supernatural ballad of the lover returned from the dead. The idea that such revenants must go again 'from the world of pity to the world without pity' when the birds cry at dawn is an ancient folklore notion that has spread from the Orient, through the Balkans, as far west as Ireland. Perhaps it is surprising to find such a rare ballad surviving as late as 1951 in the city of Birmingham, where it was recorded from an English-born singer of Irish descent. *The Grey Cock* appears as No. 248 in Child's collection,

but not in such good shape as here.

[It is not universally accepted that *The Grey Cock* is, properly speaking, a supernatural ballad at all. Hugh Shields ('The Grey Cock: Dawn Song or Revenant Ballad?' in *Ballad Studies*, ed. E. B. Lyle, 1976) examines the subject in detail, and points out that the revenant verses here have been borrowed from the Anglo-Irish broadside song *Willy-O*, a nineteenth century re-working of *Sweet William's Ghost* (Roud 50 Child 77; see, for example, Bodleian, 2806 c.15(136)). The editors have omitted Mrs Costello's penultimate verse, which also derives from *Willy-O*:

So when she saw her love disappearing
The tears down her pale cheeks in streams did flow
He said 'Weep no more for me, dear Mary
For I am no more your Willy-O'.

Although it used generally to be thought that supernatural elements tended to be dropped from ballads over time, and that their appearance was therefore indicative of greater age, there is a more recent school of thought which would hold that, in some cases at least, these elements are relatively recent accretions. This particular song may be a case in point. See also FMJ 3 (3) 1977 224-7; FSJ VIII (34) 1930 199-201 and PECS 136-7; PBB 49-50; PMB 52; PWS 86; Child IV 389-90, and Bronson IV 15-23. Two *Willy O* variants appear in DPG 48 and FMJ 3 (1) 1975 36-7.]

I Wish, I Wish

(JEFDSS VII (2) 1953 103) Roud 60 Laws P25

Most English songs tell a story. However,

there are also songs that are merely lyrical expressions of a mood – usually arising from love denied or betrayed. Such songs are not held together by any narrative; instead they employ a number of images and symbols that are combined and recombined in song after song. Thus whole songs may be made up from 'floating' verses familiar in other contexts, or attached to other melodies. The verses of *I Wish, I Wish* are most commonly found either in the song called *Waly Waly* (Roud 87 Child 204) or in *Died For Love*. Jazz enthusiasts may be interested in the apron-low, apron-high motif, which reappears in the Blues called *Careless Love*. It was also used by John Clare in *The Faithless Shepherd*, a poem largely made up of traditional 'floaters'.

[There is a whole continuum of songs containing these and other, similar, stanzas. Some versions of (for example) *The Brisk Young Lover* (or *Farmer*, or *Sailor*) and *Died For Love* also include a narrative strand in which the unfortunate girl hangs herself. Others contain elegiac verses only. Some aspects are discussed in J. W. Allen's article 'Some Notes on *O Waly Waly*' (JEFDSS VII (3) 1954 161-71), but the complex relationships of these songs, and of a large number of others which share points of detail but are probably otherwise unrelated, are largely incapable of disentanglement. See, among many examples, FSJ II (8) 1906 158-60; FSJ III (12) 1908 188-9; FSJ V (19) 181-9; FMJ 3 (2) 1976; HGG 61; HGR 46; KFBI 349; JEFDSS V (1) 1946 16-17; KTT 44-6; PECS 143-4; PMB 23, and PRVW 73. Fred Hamer's recordings of Emma Vickers (*There is a Tavern*) and May Bradley (*Willow Tree*) can be heard on, respectively, *A Century of Song* (EFDSS

CD02) and *We've Received Orders to Sail* (Topic TSCD 662).]

Jack the Jolly Tar

(FSJ II (6) 1905 39) Roud 511 Laws K40

Seafarers know this song better under the title of *Do me Ama*. Part of its appeal comes from the fact that the common sailor gets the better of the squire in such an audacious fashion. Here Jack is akin to some of the prankish heroes of the Arabian Nights, of Chaucer and Boccaccio. Mrs Hooper knew only one verse of the song. Our text is supplied from versions in common oral currency among seamen. Two other versions from Somerset and Devon are given in FSJ II (6) 1905 38-9, and Whall (WSS 16) prints an unlocated set.

[Mrs Hooper's verse ran:

I'm blowed, said Jack, if I don't venture,
I'll pull the string hanging out of her winder.
Jack came there without a shirt
And on his head a lump of dirt ...

See also FMJ 3 (2) 1976 111-2 (Sussex: one text, two tunes); DPG 24-25 (the same Sussex set); PBB 227, and *Still Growing* 66 (both William Nott's Devon set, of which one verse was omitted in FSJ II). The song persists in tradition. It appeared on broadsides as (*The*) *Jolly Jack Tar*, and (see Bodleian, Harding B 22(169)) as *The merchant's courtship to the brazier's daughter*. A similar story, though without the string, appears in Harding B 11(3373): *The sailor and nobleman*.]

John Barleycorn

(FSJ VIII (31) 1927 41) Roud 164

This ballad is rather a mystery. Is it an

unusually coherent folklore survival of the ancient myth of the slain and resurrected Corn-God, or is it the creation of an antiquarian revivalist, which has passed into the popular currency and become 'folklorized'? It is in any case an old song, of which an elaborate form was printed in the reign of James I [the ballad was licensed in 1624]. It was widespread over the English and Scottish countryside, and Burns re-wrote a well-known version. During the present century, versions have been collected in Sussex (FSJ I (3) 1901 81), Hampshire (FSJ III (13) 1909 255-6), Surrey (FSJ VI (21) 1918 27-8), Somerset (SFS III 9 and IV 32) and Wiltshire (WUP 246). The tune is a variant of that usually associated with the carol, *Dives and Lazarus*.

[The SFS IV set – one verse direct from oral tradition, the rest from Bell's *Songs of the Peasantry* – is also printed in S100 190. Further examples appear in HGG 8-9 (Bedfordshire); KFBI 608 (Shropshire); PECS 192-4 (Sussex); PCL 48-49 (Dorset), and *Still Growing* 63 (Charles Neville, Somerset). See also Bodleian, Douce Ballads 3(83a): *A pleasant new ballad to sing ev'ning and morn, of the bloody murder of sir John Barley corn*; also several later broadside editions titled *Sir John Barleycorn*. In the 1860s, Brereton of Dublin published a shortened form, *Lines written on the barley corn*. A version of the song is sung by the Lord of the Hood and his Boggins prior to the annual Haxey Hood game at the Isle of Axholme in Lincolnshire (see SMFL 16-7). There is also a later, separate song, *John Barleycorn is a Hero Bold* (Roud 2141) which appeared on broadsides and has also been found in tradition; see KFBI 609.]

Lisbon

(FSJ II (6) 1905 22) Roud 551 Laws N8

The theme of the Maiden Warrior, the girl who shows her courage on the field of battle, has held the interest of audiences since the days when the epic singers of Greece sang of Hippolyte and her Amazons. Usually, in the English ballads, the girls are impelled into battle by love, not by pugnacity. Devotion leads them to put on men's clothing and follow their serving sweethearts. The girls, though brave, are also mild, like our heroine, who is even prepared to step aside without complaint if her sweetheart finds another love while campaigning. The title of this ballad suggests that its setting is the Peninsular War of 1808, but the same story, with some identical verses, is told in the common ballad of *The Banks of the Nile* [Roud 950, Laws N9], referring to the expedition against the French in Egypt in 1801. The story is well known in Australia, but there the sailor (or soldier) has become a shearer who is obliged to leave his home for a distant shearing shed, and the girl's 'waist it is too slender and constitution too fine to eat the ram-stag mutton on the banks of the Condamine' [Roud 8224]. Traditional versions have also been reported from Sussex (FSJ II (8) 1906 191-2), Surrey (FSJ VI (21) 1918 17-18), and Dorset (FSJ VII (27) 1923 50-1).

[Verses 1, 6 and 7 here are from Mrs Lock, who had learned the song as a child from her sister-in-law. She had two more:

There I beheld a damsel, all in her bloom of years,
Making her full lamentation, her eyes did flow with tears.

'Fare thee well my best time lover, to thee it is well known,
So marry me sweet William and leave me not alone.'

'O no, my dearest Polly, pray do not go with me,
Where the soldiers they lay bleeding, it is a dismal sight;
Where the fifes and drums are beating to drown the dismal cry,
So stay at home dear Polly, and do not go with I.'

Verses 2-5 are from the set noted by H.E.D. Hammond from Mr Joseph Elliott at Todber, Dorset, in 1905 (FSJ VII (27) 1923 50-1), with, perhaps, a few details such as 'silver trumpets' and 'while she does pleasure you' adapted from a version noted by Sharp from Mrs Eliza Hutchings at Langport, Somerset, 1904 (KCSC I 552-4), or maybe from a broadside. Bodleian, Harding B 17(175b): *Lovely Nancy*, for instance, includes very similar lines, as does an earlier version, *The Maiden's Lamentation*, noted in 1778 by Timothy Connor, an American seaman imprisoned at Forton, near Portsmouth (Roy Palmer, *The Sound of History*, 276-7). There, the scene is the American War of Independence and the ship is bound for Boston; in *The Rambling Soldier* (London: Penguin, 1977 196-8) Palmer prints a later version, *The Indian War*, in which the action is transplanted to the Sikh Wars of 1845-6 and 1848-9. For further broadside editions, see Bodleian, 2806 c.13(165): *William and Nancy*; Firth c.12(165): *William and Margaret*, and Firth c.14(174): *William & Mary or The Indian war*. In this last, we move yet further forward to the Sepoy Rebellion of 1857-8. Dianne Dugaw examines the whole genre in *Warrior Women and Popular Balladry* (see bibliography).]

Long Lankin

(FSJ V (18) 1914 81) Roud 6 Child 93

In Scots versions of this bloody ballad, the hero is a mason who builds a castle, is cheated of his payment, and makes a terrible retaliation. In the English versions this idea is lost, and Lambkin, Longkin or Lankin is merely a lawless ruffian. Yet he is no ordinary robber, for it is not booty that he is after, but revenge. Is he perhaps a runaway serf with a grudge against his master? Or is he, as has been suggested, a desperate leper seeking the old folk-cure of the blood of an innocent, caught in a silver bowl? It is hard to guess the age of this ballad. Bishop Percy printed a version from Kent in 1775, and in the following year Herd published a Scottish text. The two versions differ in several details, and it is likely that the ballad was already old then. The strongest Scots tradition names Balwearie Castle as the scene – and its building in 1464 as the occasion – of the crime. Tradition is not evidence, but the song is probably based on a real event.

'Blood-boltered' as it is, Lankin retained a strong grip on the imagination of many singers, including the nun who sang the present version to Cecil Sharp. Further versions will be found in FSJ from Surrey (I (4) 1902 212-3), and Hampshire and Herefordshire (II (7) 1905 111-13). The ballad is studied in JEFDSS I (1) 1-17.

[Also in FSJ V 83 (and S100 62-4, modified) was a set noted by Sharp from Yarrow Gill, Ely Workhouse, Cambridgeshire, in 1911. The editors have replaced Sister Emma's verse 14 with one of Mr Yarrow's, and the seventeenth verse here is also from him. Sister Emma sang

How can I come down, 'tis so late in the night
There's no fire burning nor candle to give light.

A set recorded by Bob Copper from Ben Butcher of Hampshire appears in JEFDSS IX (2) 1961 74-5, and can be heard on Topic Records, *O'er his Grave the Grass Grew Green* (TSCD 653, 1998). A version recorded by Tom Munnelly from John Reilly, County Roscommon, is in FMJ 3 (1) 1975 15-17, and on the cassette *Songs of the Irish Travellers: Traditional Ballads and Lyric Songs* (Dublin: European Ethnic Oral Traditions, (1983); and the Hampshire set referred to above is also printed in PRVW 47. See also Child II 320-94 and Bronson II 428-445. For a broadside edition, see Bodleian, Harding B 25(1048): *The lambkin* (reprinted in ED&S 63 (2) 2001 7).

The ballad has lasted particularly well in the USA, where a large number of examples have been found. John DeWitt Niles ('*Lamkin*: The Motivation of Horror', *Journal of American Folklore* 90 1977 49-67) makes the interesting suggestion that 'Lambkin' may be a deliberately oblique name, of the sort applied to the fairies ('the good folk') or the Devil ('the Old Boy'), and that he may have started out as a supernatural being, contracted to build a castle and, having been denied his due fee – not money, but human life – collected it for himself.

There is less of a tendency today to read arcane meanings into ballads. Tradition has attached *Lankin* to a number of physical locations, including Nafferton Tower in Northumberland, but its appeal has been primarily as a compelling and universal horror-story; certainly it has been, over a great many years, 'the terror of countless nurseries', as Child commented. Niles' opening comments put it nicely:

'Everyone loves a good killing. The more bloody and cruel the killing, the more interesting it is likely to be, especially when the victims are helpless: a woman alone, an infant child. But the most fascinating murder of all, to the popular mind, is a bloody killing of helpless persons *with no plausible motive*.'

With regard to the basin, Roy Palmer (PRVW 49) comments appositely, 'The superstitious dread of allowing noble blood to be spilt on the ground was apparently more powerful than the inhibition on killing nobles.']

Lord Thomas and Fair Eleanor
(FSJ II (7) 1905 109) Roud 4 Child 73

The theme of this ballad is banal enough: a triangular love-affair that ends in the death of all three lovers. It is the characters that hold the imagination – weak, fickle Lord Thomas, haughty, fair Eleanor, and the dark, vengeful bride with the dagger hidden in her wedding dress. During this century the ballad has quite frequently been found over an area bounded by Devon, Hertfordshire, Herefordshire and Staffordshire. Also several Scottish sets are known. It is interesting that most of the English versions, and all the numerous American ones, obviously derive from a broadside text published during the reign of Charles II and often reprinted. Scholars incline to consider oral transmission to be almost a *sine qua non* of folk song diffusion, but ballads such as this remind us that word-of-mouth is far from being the only way in which folk songs have been traditionally passed on. In Scotland this ballad is sometimes called *Fair Annet*. It must be said that some of the Scottish oral versions hold beauties lacking in the texts under influence of print: such, for instance, as this embellishment to the description of Annet's grand journey to Lord Thomas's wedding:

There were four and twenty gray goshawks
A-flaffin their wings sae wide,
To flaff the stour fra aff the road
That fair Annie did ride.

In the version of the text printed here, Mrs Pond's words have been expanded from versions collected by Hammond from Mrs [Mary] Rowsell, of Taunton, Somerset, in 1905 (FSJ II (7) 1905 105) and by Sharp from Mrs [Emily] Cockram, of Meshaw, Devon, in 1904 (FSJ II (7) 1905 107). Other versions have been found in oral tradition in Hampshire (FSJ II (7) 1905 106), Somerset (FSJ II (7) 1905 109), Hertfordshire (FSJ V (19) 1915 130-1), Staffordshire (BSFL 651 [reprinted in PBB 79-82]), and Gloucestershire (WUP 135-7). Kidson (KTT 40) reports a Yorkshire version with words from a broadside of *c*.1740.

[Mrs Pond had nine verses, of which three only were printed in the *Journal*. They correspond to verses 8, 15 and 16 here, and appeared thus:

'A hundred of thy friends dear child,
A hundred of thy foes,
Before I beg thee with all my blessing
For Lord Thomas his wedding don't go!'

Lord Thomas, he walked up and down in the room,
With his sword hung by his side;
He took off the brown girl's head from her shoulders,
And flung it against the wall.

'There's one towards the brown girl,' he cried,
'There's another towards my heart;'
There is never three lovers should meet together
Whatever shall soon depart.

Thirteen stanzas were quoted from Mrs Rowsell, and ten from Mrs Cockram, following on from Mrs Rowsell's eleventh stanza. Our verses 1-4, 6, 7, 9 and 13 are from Mrs Rowsell; verses 5, 10-12, 14 and 16-18 are from Mrs Cockram. Verse 15 is a collation of material from Mrs Pond and Mrs Cockram. Mrs Cockram's set is given in full in KCSC I 69-71.

The editors name no source for the stanza quoted from a 'Scottish oral version'; it is, however, quite close to one given in Motherwell's *Minstrelsy*, p. lxviii, 19, from 'some traditionary copies', and quoted in Child II 195. This very popular ballad appeared on a range of broadsides and songsters from the seventeenth century to the nineteenth. See Bodleian, Douce Ballads 1(120b) for a London broadside example of 1677, *A tragical story of lord Thomas and fair Ellinor*. Later editions can be found as *A tragical ballad of the unfortunate loves of lord Thomas and fair Eleanor*, and as *Lord Thomas and Fair Eleanor*. Much the same story is also found in Scandinavian tradition (*Herr Peder och Liten Kerstin* and other titles), and in France (*Les Tristes Noces* and others). See also CSB 44-5; S100 65-7 (collated from several versions noted by Sharp); Child II 179-199, and Bronson II 88-154.]

Lovely Joan

(FSJ IV (15) 1910 90) Roud 592

Many of our amatory folk songs show a double sentiment of gaiety and irony that comes as a surprise to those expecting merely yokel quaintness. The young lady may show herself at a loss over the conduct of a false lover, but, confronted with importunity, she remains as a rule unruffled, completely mistress of herself. And if the subterfuges she adopts are of doubtful honesty, the implied judgement is that she is a smart girl and it serves that young fellow right. Thus, *Lovely Joan* seems to be sister of such resourceful girls as the heroine of the *Broomfield Hill* or of the traditional sets of *Blow Away the Morning Dew*. The song has been taken from oral tradition in Sussex (FSJ I (5) 1904 270), Suffolk (FSJ IV (17) 1913 330), Somerset (SFS IV 48), and Wiltshire (WUP 46). The text, hitherto published only in modified form, is completed here from the MS collection of Cecil Sharp.

[Only one full verse from Mr Jay was printed in the *Journal*:

For she did not think herself quite safe,
No, not until she came to her true love's gate.
But she's robbed him all of his stores of gold,
And left him the empty purse to hold.

Much of the additional text here came from Jim Proll (Prole), Monksilver, Somerset, 1906 (KCSC II 60; SFS above, and S100 130-1, modified); rather 'pol-ished up' by the editors. The first verse appears to be from Henry Hills, late of Lodsworth, Sussex (FSJ I above, with 'One noble knight' altered to 'A fine young man'), and lines 3 and 4 in verse 2 seem to have been introduced from a set of the similar, but probably unrelated, song *Sweet Kitty* (Roud 1349) noted by Sharp from Captain Lewis of Minehead, Somerset, in 1906 (JEFDSS VIII (4) 1959 201, KCSC II 107-8 and S100 72-3, collated). The 'pooks of hay' occur in neither traditional nor broadside examples of *Lovely Joan*, and have likely been borrowed by the editors from a set of *Blow Away the Morning Dew* (Child 112, Roud 11) noted by Sharp from Lucy White and Louie Hooper at Hambridge, Somerset, in 1903 (FSJ II (6) 1905 18 and S100 46-7, collated). Other modifications of uncertain provenance, such as the final two lines, may be wholly editorial. Further sets (Hampshire and Norfolk) appear in PCL 95-6 and PRVW 127-8. See also, among several broadside examples, Bodleian, Harding B 11(2225).]

Lucy Wan

(JEFDSS I (1) 1932 53) Roud 234 Child 51

This rare ballad, also called *Lizzie Wan*, belongs to the same tradition as the well-known *Edward*. But whereas in *Edward* it is usually the brother who is the victim (for reasons that are seldom clear), in *Lizzie* or *Lucy Wan* it is the sister, guilty of incest whether wittingly or not, who is savagely put to death. This is the only version of the ballad found in oral tradition in England, nor has any new Scottish version been reported since the publication of Motherwell's *Minstrelsy* in 1827. The ballad is No. 51 in Child. The three opening stanzas are quoted from Child (with 'Lucy' substituted for 'Lizzie'), and the order of Mrs Dann's verses is rearranged for the sake of coherence.

[Mrs Dann repeated the second half of each verse, though that feature has been dropped here. She had only the second part of our verse four, and the first two lines are again taken from Child I 448, version 51A. She also had an additional half verse:

O, what did he do there? you very soon shall hear.
He shed poor Lucy's blood.

She didn't recall where, or from whom, she had learned the song. Ella Bull commented that a number of Scottish prisoners had been quartered in the area 'in Cromwell's time' and some had subsequently settled locally, which she thought might explain the song's presence there. A very fragmentary set was noted by George Gardiner in Hampshire, 1908. It was published, extensively re-constructed, in PCL 81-2. An additional Scottish example, noted in the late 1820s, appears in Emily B. Lyle (ed.), *Andrew Crawfurd's Collection of Ballads and Songs*, Edinburgh: Scottish Text Society 1975, I 115-17, and several versions have been found in the USA. See Child I 447-449 and Bronson 403-6.]

The Manchester 'Angel'

(FSJ VII (27) 1923 52) Roud 2741

The Angel Inn is said to have stood in the Market Place adjoining Market Sted Lane, Manchester. According to Miss Anne Gilchrist, 'it seems possible that this song dates from about the '45. In November 1745 a Manchester regiment was raised in support of Charles Edward's cause, but suffered disaster with the Prince after the fiasco at Derby, surrendering at Carlisle a few weeks later.' Other versions of the song have been found in Dorset (FSJ VII (27) 1923 52-3) and in Yorkshire (KP 4 and FSJ VII (27) 1923 54).

[The final verse here has been altered, perhaps with reference to that given in CPM 734. Mr Gregory had only the first and fourth lines of verse 1, and in this and several other verses editorial modifications from unidentified sources have been made.

See Bodleian, Harding B 11(2388), Harding B 11(3575), Harding B 25(1801) and others: *The Soldier's Farewell to Manchester*; Harding B 11(2306) and Harding B 25(1206): *The Manchester Girl*; and Harding B 28(14): *In coming down to Manchester*. Verses from this song also appear in broadside editions of *The Streams of Lovely Nancy*, q.v.]

The Man of Burningham Town

(FSJ IV (15) 1910 85) Roud 665

Another homilectic ballad that, like *The Daughter of Peggy* and *On Monday Morning*, treats of a drastic cure for errant wives. Among H. E. D. Hammond's manuscripts is a version of this song (called *The Man of Dover*) collected in Dorset in 1905. E. J. Moeran published a Norfolk version (FSJ VII (26) 1922 8). Our words are filled out from these two sets. The singer sang 'Burningham', apparently meaning Burnham (on Crouch), not Birmingham.

[Verses 3, 8 (modified) and 9 here are from Harry Cox of Catfield, Norfolk; his set appeared in the *Journal* as *In Burnham*

Town. Burnham on Crouch is in Essex, but there are four Burnhams in Norfolk. The song was printed in the *Journal* as *Birmingham Boys*, which may after all have been the right guess; it was published on broadsides as *The Merry Jilt; or, The Birmingham Boys*; though also as *The Bermondsey Boys*. A version collated from three sets noted by Hammond was later printed in PWS 74 (J. Pomeroy, Bridport, Dorset 1906, with material from Mrs Gulliver, Combe Florey, Somerset 1905 and Mrs Russell, Upwey, Dorset 1907); see also PRVW 112 (Mr Locke, collated) and KFBI 451 (Harry Cox).]

The Mermaid

(FSJ III (10) 1907 47) Roud 124 Child 289

The superstition that the sight of a mermaid is an omen of shipwreck is ancient and widespread, yet songs that treat of it are few. There is no sign that *The Mermaid* is older than the eighteenth century, but it has persisted in many forms, in both England and Scotland, in oral tradition, on broadsides, in song-books. It has been used as a sea-shanty, also as a students' song and a children's game ('The big ship sails up the Alley, Alley O'). Perhaps because of its familiarity in print, commentators and collectors have rather neglected this song, which, in good versions, has its fine points. The ballad is No. 289 in Child. It has been reported in recent years, from Oxfordshire (WUP 84), Hampshire (Gillington, *Old Hampshire Singing Games*), Cheshire (FSJ III (10) 1907 49), Dorset (FSJ III (10) 1907 50-1), Devonshire (FSJ III (11) 1907 139), and, in a common fragment, from Berkshire (FSJ V (19) 1915 227).

[Mr Herridge (or Herage) omitted the second line of verse four; this was added by the collector, E. T. Sweeting. Verses 6-8 here have been added by the editors; 6 and 7 are probably modifications of verses from a set printed in *The Child's Own Singing Book* of 1843 (FSJ III (10) 1907 47) and 8 is from *The Seaman's Distress* of *c*.1765 (Child V 149 version 289A; Ashton, *Real Sailor Songs* 1891 42, and PBC 127-8). The ballad has been found widely in the USA and Canada. See also Child V 148-152 and Bronson IV 370-87. A number of broadside editions can be seen at the Bodleian collection as *The Mermaid*. Seemingly ancestral is a seventeenth century broadside ballad, *The praise of saylors here set forth*; for which, see Bodleian, 4o Rawl. 566(157).]

Mother, Mother, Make my Bed

(FSJ V (19) 1915 135-7) Roud 45 Child 65

There has been some argument whether this ballad derives from *Lady Maisry* or *Lord Lovel* [Roud 48 Child 75). The manner of the lady's impending death, which would provide the essential clue, is missing. We do not know whether she is to be put to death on account of her disgrace (like Lady Maisry) or is pining for her lover's absence (like Lord Lovel's sweetheart). It hardly matters. In the version of Mrs Ford, a Sussex blacksmith's wife, the ballad is a good one. It has also been found in Somerset (FSJ I (2) 1900 44), Dorset (FSJ III (11) 1907 74-6) and Hampshire (FSJ III (13) 1909 304-6).

[Mrs Ford learned the song from her mother. Cecil Sharp noted several other versions in both England and the Appalachians. MacColl and Seeger, *Travellers' Songs from England and Scotland*

112, print a set from 'Queen' Caroline Hughes, and point out that this song seems to be a collage of ballad formulae, 'selected and put together in a form which has remained stable.' A further version, *The Little Footman Boy*, recorded in the 1970s by Mike Yates from Alice Penfold of Sussex, has recently been issued on Musical Traditions MTCD320, *Here's Luck to a Man*.]

The New York Trader

(FSJ VII (26) 1922 2)

Roud 478 Laws K22A/K22B

Britain has a group of ballads in which a criminal on board a ship is detected by supernatural means. These include *Brown Robyn's Confession* (Child 57 Roud 3882), *The Gosport Tragedy* (Roud 15 Laws P36A/B), *Sir William Gower*, and *William Glenn*, with which the *New York Trader* is sometimes confused. In fact, all three latter songs seem to derive from an older ballad called *The Pirate*, in which the ship is bound for New Barbary, not for 'New York in Ameriky'. *The New York Trader* evidently enjoyed a vogue in the nineteenth century. It was frequently published by provincial broadside firms, and Catnach, in London, found it worth issuing at least three times. Alfred Williams collected a version in Wiltshire (WUP 265-6) and Cecil Sharp reported two Somerset versions of the closely related *Sir William Gower* (FSJ V (18) 1914 46-7). The ballad called *The Sailor and the Ghost* or *The Man and the Two Maidens* (FSJ VII (27) 1923 46-7: Roud 568 Laws P34A) belongs to the same family of songs.

[Mr Goffin's text was very close to broadside editions. The editors have omitted his second verse:

On the first of March we did set sail,
With a sweet and a pleasant gale,
With hearts undaunted we put to sea,
Bound for New York in Ameriky.

For two Catnach broadsides, see Bodleian, Johnson Ballads 220 and Harding B 11(2163). There are also editions from Birt, Such, and Hodges (all London). *Sir William Gower* and *William Glenn* are also grouped as Roud 478 and Laws K22A/B. Palmer (PBC 141) prints a garland text, *Captain Glen's Unhappy Voyage*, of c.1770. Bronson II 24-28 prints versions of *William Guiseman*, *Captain* or *William Glen*, *Sir William Gower* and *The New York Trader*, as an appendix to *Brown Robyn's Confession* (Child 57 Roud 3882); see also Child II 13-16.

The reference above to 'an older ballad called *The Pirate*' is curious, as nothing by that name seems to fit the bill, but *William Grismond* may perhaps be meant. This was a broadside of c.1650 which Child cited as probably ancestral to the group. Anne Gilchrist, in notes to Mr Goffin's set, mentioned that 'High Barbary' was the destination of the ship in earlier versions, and referred to sets of *William Glen* and *William Guiseman* (a later, Scottish form of *William Grismond*) printed in Dean Christie's *Traditional Ballad Airs* (1876, I 240 and 1881, II 172); Christie in turn mentions that Walter Scott quoted from *William Glen* in his novel, *The Pirate* (chapter 36; two verses) and it may perhaps be that the titles became confused during the preparation of this book. See Bodleian, Wood 401(155): *The downfall of William Grismond, or, A lamentable murder by him committed at Lainterdine in the County of Hereford the 22 of March, 1650.*]

O Shepherd, O Shepherd

(FSJ III (11) 1907 122) Roud 1055

From the form of this song, Miss Anne Gilchrist suspected that it may once have been a singing game – perhaps in the form of the advancing and retiring line – with one person playing the shepherd to whom inducements are offered to persuade him to return home. Various early Scottish compilers (Johnson, Herd, Chambers) printed versions of the song, though we have found no other English set than this. The tune is interesting as being a modal version of *Greensleeves*. Either the well-known version is a modal tune 'improved' by an ignorant musician, or else it has been converted into a modal tune by a country singer.

[Mrs Davis sometimes substituted 'Basin of broth' for 'Bread and cheese'. In fact, Hammond noted two sets, the other being from William Bartlett at Wimbourne, Dorset, 1905 (see REC 196-7), together with a further example of the tune, and Alfred Williams got a version in Gloucestershire (WUP 176-7). Mrs Davis' penultimate verse appeared in the *Journal*, tactfully amended and in brackets, as:

Oh! your house is clean swept and your true love's there...

The editors have restored the proper reading from Hammond's MSS (D705). Mrs Davis' text, set to a tune from Charles Drake, also of Dorchester, appears in PCL 90.]

The Old Man From Lee

(JEFDSS III (2) 1937 130) Roud 362

The old man's courtship is an ancient joke of which country folk never seemed to tire. In a form similar to the one we publish, the song appeared in the *Musical Miscellany* (London) in 1730. It seems to be widespread in Scotland, and Sharp found it common in the West Country. Versions have been reported from Yorkshire (KTT 92; FSJ II (9) 1906 273), Worcestershire (*Folklore* X 173-4) and Wiltshire (WUP 73). Our text is amplified from the Wiltshire version.

[The 'Yorkshire versions' are really *Maids, When You're Young Never Wed An Old Man* (Roud 210); a separate song on a similar theme. Verses 1, 2, 5 and 6 here are from the *Journal*; there was another verse noted by Dr McCleay, who wrote it down 'from memory of the singing of an old man in Coggeshall, Essex, from whom he heard it about fifty years ago', but it was not printed. The *Journal* editor, Frank Howes, commented:

'I do not mind the obscenity of the last verse but I have shrunk from the indelicacy of the one before. It is a theme that lends itself to simple salacity and it is important that the existence of this strain in English folk song should be realised by others than the collectors in the field who cannot fail to encounter it sooner or later. It is to be found in this song.'

Verses 3 and 4 here are from the text noted by Alfred Williams from Mrs Russell, late of Crudwell, Wiltshire (1914-16). The identity of the expunged verse remains a mystery for the present; perhaps the offending lines were something like these, here anglicised from the version sung by the renowned Scottish singer Jeannie Robertson (see KFBI 316):

My mother told me to give him a kiss.
Eh, but I'll not have him.

If you like him so well you can kiss him yourself...

Howes would have been well aware of the secondary meaning often accorded the word 'kiss' in old songs. A set noted by Gardiner in Hampshire, 1908, appears in PMB 65. The song has also been found widely in the USA and Canada.]

On Monday Morning

(FSJ III (13) 1909 315) Roud 433 Laws Q6

Baring-Gould, who describes this as a song 'relished by married men', found an early set in a collection of stall balladry, *West Country Garlands*, date about 1760. He obtained a version from the singing of Robert Hard of South Brent, Devon, which he called *A Week's Work Well Done* (BGSW 238-9). Our version is sung to a variant of the well-known *Turpin Hero* tune. Frank Kidson had information that the song was sung by Grimaldi the Clown, about 1820.

[A second version – tune only – was also given in FSJ III. Other sets appear as *A Week's Work Well Done* (PMB 98), *The Holly Twig* (PRVW 106), and *The Batchelor* (SYB I, 7). The song has also been found quite widely in the USA. For a broadside edition, *Week's Work Completed*, see Bodleian, Harding B 25(2022). There have been a number of variations on the basic theme; see, for example, Firth c.26(51): *Woeful Marriage*; Harding B 20(185): *Weeks Matrimony*; and Harding B 11(1666): *I Was Married a Week* (in which the sexes are reversed).]

One Night as I Lay on My Bed

(FSJ III (11) 1907 78) Roud 672

This piece belongs to a sizeable family of night-visit songs (called *Fensterlieder* – window songs – in Germany). It is related in theme to the well-known *Go from my Window, Go,* quoted in Beaumont and Fletcher's *Knight of the Burning Pestle* (1613), and before that, parodied as a sacred piece in *Ane Compendious Booke of Godly and Spirituall Songs* (1567). There, the scene is translated to Paradise. The importunate caller at the window is a sinner whom God first refuses but eventually admits by the door. Burns found a three-verse fragment, resembling part of our Dorset version, which he sent to Johnson for publication in *The Scots Musical Museum*, and, on the evidence of Allan Cunningham's *Works of Burns* (1834), the poet probably knew another version, from Nithsdale, ending with the familiar lovers' vow that the seas shall dry and the fishes fly and the rocks melt in the sun before one proves false to the other. Baring-Gould prints a Devonshire version of *Go from my Window*, with the words re-written, under the title *Come to my Window*. Barrett has a version in BF described by Miss Margaret Dean-Smith as 'little altered since (it) appeared in the *Fitzwilliam Virginal Book*'. A Sussex fragment collected by W. P. Merrick is in FSJ I (3) 1901 269. The Somerset song *Arise Arise you Drowsy Sleeper* in SFS IV [and S100 106-7, collated] is also related. From stanza 2 onward, our text is from Mr House of Beaminster, Dorset, collected by H. E. D. Hammond in 1906 (FSJ III (11) 1907 79-80).

[Mrs Russell had only two verses. The second, not used here, was:

Then my love arose and went his way,
My dad and mam a-grumbling lay
Saying 'Who is there that makes such ado?'

Replied the maid so fair,
'Hark! how the wind doth blow.'

This song has been reported only rarely; apart from the two Dorset examples mentioned, and the Scottish fragment, Dr Gardiner noted it in Southampton in 1907 (REC 201) and Maud Karpeles found a version in Newfoundland in 1929 (Karpeles, *Folk Songs from Newfoundland*, London: Faber, 1971 239-40). The editors' references to *Go from My Window* (Roud 966) and *Drowsy Sleeper* (Roud 402, Laws M4; to which latter group the Sussex fragment mentioned above also seems to belong) should probably not be taken as implying anything more than a very general thematic relationship.]

The Outlandish Knight

(FSJ IV (15) 1910 123) Roud 21 Child 4

This ballad has many titles. Scholars know it as *Lady Isabel and the Elf Knight* or *May Colvin*, but *An Outlandish Rover*, *The Highway Robber*, *The Old Beau*, are among titles preferred by folk singers. Child, who published it as No. 4 in his collection, noted it as one of the most widespread of ballads, with relatives in Poland, Germany, Scandinavia, France, the Netherlands (as *Halewijn*), and elsewhere, as far afield as Australia. It is also among the most persistent, being not infrequently sung today. Some scholars see in it traces of the Bluebeard story, others believe it may be an offshoot of the legend of Judith and Holofernes. Perhaps more plausible is the theory that the ballad is descended from a folk-tale about a malevolent water-spirit who transforms himself into a knight and marries a girl with the intention of car-

rying her off to his watery home. The genial incident of the dialogue with the parrot (borrowed from Oriental tradition?) was isolated and made into a comic stage song, called *Tell-Tale Polly* (*c*. 1860). Within this century, besides our Norfolk set, versions have been printed from Westmorland (FSJ II (9) 1906 282), Yorkshire (three versions, FSJ II (9) 1906 282-3), Herefordshire (FSJ IV (15) 1910 122), Hertfordshire (FSJ IV (15) 1910 118), Sussex (FSJ IV (15) 1910 121), Wiltshire (WUP 159-161), and Somerset (four versions, FSJ IV (15) 1910 119-121; Sharp reported that he had found 23 sets of it in that county), Devon (FSJ IV (15) 1910 119) and Cornwall (FSJ IV (15) 1910 116-117). A fragmentary version in Manx is printed in FSJ VII (30) 1926 301.

[RVW noted no words from Mr Hilton beyond 'She borrowed some of her father's gold'. The editors have instead adapted the bulk of the text from Cornwall referred to above, noted by C. S. Parsonson from Mr Lugg of Launceston in 1905, with additional verses added from other sources. Verses 3, 4, 5, 7, 9, 10 and 14 are based on Mr Lugg's, while verse 12 is essentially the Hertfordshire stanza mentioned above, noted by Ada R. Broadwood from 'an old village woman' at St. Stephen's around 1895. Other verses are fairly standard, appearing in similar forms in both traditional and broadside examples. In verses 7 and 8, Mr Lugg sang 'prickle'; the editors have restored the 'sickle' that appears in some versions as part of the heroine's ruse. Traditional singers often speak, rather than sing, parts of their songs; most typically the final lines, but not unusually other parts also. Mr Lugg spoke our verse 14, thus:

'Nothing, master, but the old cat's on the top of my cage, to take my sweet life away, and I'm calling on my young mistress to drive the old puss away.'

Other versions are in Bruce & Stokoe, *Northumbrian Minstrelsy* 48-50; FMJ 3 (1) 1975 17-19; HGG 50-1 and ED&S 28 (1) 1966 22; KTT 26-8 and 172; PECS 109-11; S100 28-31; SFML 20-1, and SLM 58. The song was widely printed on broadsides. See, among others, Bodleian, Firth c.21(15): *Outlandish Knight*; and Harding B 16(234b): *The Old Beau's Courtship*. *Tell-tale Polly*, from *Charley Fox's Minstrel's Companion* (Philadelphia: Turner & Fisher, 1858) is quoted in Bronson I 50 No. 4.25. Beside extensive entries in Child I 22-62 and Bronson I 39-100, the song-family is examined in detail in Holger Nygard's book *The Ballad of 'Heer Halewijn', Its Forms and Variations in Western Europe: A Study of the History and Nature of a Ballad Tradition* (Knoxville: University of Tennessee Press, 1958), also published as FF Communications, No. 169 (Helsinki: Suomalainen Tiedeakatemia/ Academia Scientiarum Fennica, 1958). His opinion was that the ballad came to Britain via France, where it is commonly known as *Renaud le Tueur de Femmes*, and that its oldest forms were those found in the Netherlands.]

T'Owd Yowe wi' one Horn

(FSJ II (7) 1905 79) Roud 1762

The words of this song do not amount to much more than a mild piece of country humour. It may be a come-down version of a once-impressive piece, but if so, its former glory has faded out of sight. Yet the shape of the verse and the classical ballad ring of the tune indicate a noble ancestry. We print it mainly for the sake of the melody, which deserves wider recognition. At the same time, many will smile at the mutton-headed pugnacity of the indomitable 'owd yowe'. Percy Grainger recorded this at a folk-song competition in Brigg, Lincolnshire. It won third prize. This seems to be the only version recorded from oral tradition.

[The editors have polished up the lyric a little. The competition took place at the North Lincolnshire Musical Competition Festival; 1905 was the first year there had been a folk song category. Frank Kidson was the judge, and awarded first prize to Joseph Taylor for his performance of *Creeping Jane* (Roud 1012 Laws Q23), a 1908 recording of which can be heard on Topic Records, *A Story I'm Just About to Tell* (TSCD 658); William Hilton came second with *Come All You Merry Ploughboys* (Roud 202; see SYB I 49-50). Kidson commented of *T'Owd Yowe*, 'This absurd production has at least what appears to be a very early air associated with it.'

The Pindar was a local official responsible for penning stray livestock.]

Oxford City

(FSJ II (8) 1906 162) Roud 218 Laws P30

Perhaps this song celebrated a real life tragedy. It often appeared on broadsides in the nineteenth century, published by Catnach and Such, of London, Harkness of Preston, and Jackson of Birmingham. Other versions have been found in oral tradition in Essex (FSJ II (8) 1906 157), Sussex (FSJ II (8) 1906 200), and Dorset (FSJ VII (27) 1923 41), with two further texts from Somerset and Dorset, collected by H.E.D. Hammond (FSJ VII (27) 1923 42-3). Our text is completed from these several versions.

[A popular song, still to be found in tradition; also known as *Worcester City*, *Newport Street*, *Jealousy*, and *Poison in a Glass of Wine*. Further versions appear in JEFDSS 9 (4) 1963 194-5 (Sussex); ED&S 29 (2) 1967 (Devon); KFBI 715; HGG 36 and 53 (Bedfordshire and Shropshire); PBB 172 (Staffordshire); PCL 46-7 (Hampshire); SMFL 28-9, and SLM 59 (Sussex).

Only Mr Harper's tune was published in the *Journal*. The text here has been re-shaped by the editors, using mainly material from FSJ VII (*Although My Name it is Maria*: Mrs Gulliver, Combe Florey, Somerset, 1905, and *In Midfordshire*: Mr Slade, Dorchester, Dorset, 1905), with a little added from FSJ II (*Oxford City*: Mrs Verrall, Horsham, Sussex, 1904).

The broadside editions referred to can be seen, with others, at the Bodleian collection. *Oxford City*: Johnson Ballads 245 (Catnach); Harding B 11(161) (Such); Harding B 11(2900A) (Harkness), and Firth b.34(220) (Jackson); and *The Newport Street Damsel*: Harding B 25(1344).]

The Ploughman

(FSJ II (8) 1906 190) Roud 2538

This song started out, as some songs will, with intent to end otherwise. Mr Burstow's first verse was originally:

It's of a pretty wench that came running 'long a trench,
And sweetheart she could not get one,
'When there's many a dirty sow a

sweetheart has got now,
And I, a pretty wench, can't get one, get one, get one,
And I, a pretty wench, can't get one.'

Here we are on familiar ground, for the beginning is that of the well-known *Condescending Lass*, often printed on broadsides, and not infrequently met with in the mouths of country singers to this day. The *Condescending Lass* belongs to the sizeable family of songs on the theme of 'I wouldn't marry a ...'. In it the girl reviews men of various trades, and rejects them all until she finds one whom she will deign to consider. But the present version loses sight of this theme, and from verse two onwards forgets all about the pernickety girl, settling down to a eulogy of the ploughman's trade, though here and there the words still recall those of *The Condescending Lass*. For the sake of coherence we have abandoned Mr Burstow's first verse and given it another title (he called it: *Pretty Wench*). A Wiltshire version is given in WUP 122.

[ODNR (1992 edition, 423) quotes the following from *Gammer Gurton's Garland*, 1784:

I am a pretty wench,
And I come from a great way hence,
And sweethearts I can get none:
But every dirty sow
Can get sweethearts enough,
And I pretty wench can get none.

In her notes to Mr Burstow's song, Lucy Broadwood commented, 'This tune should be compared with *There was a Pretty Lass, and a Tenant of my Own* in Chappell's *Popular Music*' (CPM II 595-6). 'Chappell states that that air was introduced into very many ballad-operas, and also that the ballad is printed on broadsides with music under the title of *The condescending Lass.*' Chappell quotes the tune, but with a text from the 1733 ballad opera *The Livery Rake*; he does not enlarge on the content of *The Condescending Lass*. It is not clear whether or not Miss Broadwood had seen the broadside itself (there is one copy in the British Library), or, indeed, whether our editors had seen it. Be that as it may, subsequent writers have tended to use the title when referring to *Pretty Wench* and its possible relatives; Dave Harker, for example, prints three texts in *Songs from the Manuscript Collection of John Bell* (Publications of the Surtees Society, vol. CXVI 1985 199-200) under the working title of *Pretty Wench*, and Lloyd himself included a verse from one (sung in this case to the tune of *Corn Rigs*) in *Come All Ye Bold Miners* (revised edition, 1978, p. 315):

The pitmen are not bonny lads.
The pitmen are not bonny O.
If they're ever sae clean, yet they're black aboot the een,
And I like them the worst o' ony, O.]

Ratcliffe Highway

(FSJ II (8) 1906 172) Roud 598

In the first half of the nineteenth century, Ratcliffe Highway, Stepney, was the toughest thoroughfare in the East End of London. It was a place of sailors' lodging-houses, sailors' pubs, sailors' ladies. Henry Mayhew has given us vivid descriptions of the Highway, with tall brazen-faced women dressed in gaudy colours, sly pimps and crimps, roaring sailors out for a good time, bearded foreign musicians from the fifteen dance halls of the locality, and the intrepid policemen of H Division walking through the throng in twos. The *Ratcliffe Highway* song may have been made for performances in ships foc'sles, or it may have been made to impress the patrons of the Eastern Music Hall, the British Queen, the Prussian Eagle, or another local public house licensed for music. In any case, it has now some ring of the tradition and much of the ring of truth. Mrs Howard's text is supplemented from an unpublished version collected in Sussex in 1954 and kindly communicated by R. Copper, and from a broadside by Catnach.

[The song appeared on broadsides from the 1820s onward, as *Rolling Down Wapping*. For the Catnach edition, see Bodleian, Harding B 11(3307A). See also *Change for a Guinea* (Harding B 28 (194)). RVW had considerable difficulty noting Mrs Howard's words (verses 1, 2, 3 and 7 here, modified), commenting: 'It was impossible to take down the words of this song at all accurately, and at the best they are fragmentary.' A Hampshire set was printed in CL 75; also augmented from the Catnach broadside. See also PBC 204-5 (William Bolton) and PBB 159-60. Mr Bolton told Anne Gilchrist that 'in his young days it was a favourite diversion among sailors ashore to take a walk down the highway, and if their hearts were not cheered by the sight of some fight or disturbance already going on, to set about creating one without delay!' (Gilchrist Collection, AGG/7/273B).]

The Red Herring

(FSJ V (20) 1916 284) Roud 128

A nonsense song of the sort of *The*

Mallard [Roud 1517], *The Jolly Old Hawk* [Roud 1048], *The Sow Took the Measles* [Roud 128], and *The Hunting of the Wren* [Roud 236] (a well-known foreign relative is the French-Canadian *Alouette*). Perhaps at one time these pieces were by no means nonsensical, but accompanied a magic ritual connected with a sacred beast. The primitive dance tunes usually associated with this kind of song, remarked upon by Miss Lucy Broadwood, may point to a former ceremonial use. Whatever the case, to singers nowadays *The Red Herring* is merely a piece of amiable tomfoolery. Cecil Sharp printed three versions from Somerset (FSJ V (20) 1916, 283-5) and a version from Wiltshire is in WUP 167.

[Only one verse from Mr Trump – the first here – appeared in the *Journal*. The editors seem to have used most of Alfred Williams' composite text (from 'Wassail' Harvey, Cricklade, and Elijah Iles, Inglesham) for the rest, rewriting it to conform to the pattern of Mr Trump's version and substituting 'blooming' for 'Aylesbury'. One verse is probably based on part of Louie Hooper's set (FSJ V (20) 1916 283-4):

O what do you think I made out of my red herring's navel?
As good an old putt as ever drawed gravel ...

Roy Palmer, PRVW 43, states 'the earliest printing of the song seems to have been in 1895, though a manuscript copy was taken down as early as 1831.' Other versions appear in ED&S 36 (1) 1974 19, HGG 16-17, HGGR 23-4, KFBI 651, PECS 227-8, and PWS 52.]

Robin Hood and the Pedlar

(FSJ II (8) 1906 156) Roud 333 Child 132

The text given here is very slightly amended from that collected by Lucy Broadwood from Mr Burstow of Horsham, Sussex [FSJ I (4) 1902 144-5]. The song of Robin Hood's encounter with the battling pedlar was printed on broadsides by Such and Catnach in the nineteenth century, in much the same version as Mr Burstow sang it. In earlier forms of this ballad (as in Child 128 [Roud 3956, *Robin Hood Newly Revived*]) the outlaw's redoubtable antagonist is not a pedlar but a young gentleman dressed in silk, with stockings of shining scarlet, named Young Gamwell. 'Gamwell' and 'Gamble Gold' are thought to be corruptions of Gamelyn, and the story may be a come-down fragment of the manuscript *Tale of Gamelyn* (*c*.1340). Other versions are printed from Essex (FSJ II (8) 1906 155) and Sussex (FSJ V (18) 1914 94).

[The editors have changed Mr Burstow's 'gay green silks' – the usual phrase in traditional and broadside versions – to 'gay green cloth'. The song, which seems first to appear in print in this form in the nineteenth century, has also been found in tradition in the USA and Canada, and as recently as the 1960s in Sussex (PECS 81-3) and Gloucestershire (Musical Traditions, *Band of Gold*, MT CD 307, 2000). See also FMJ 3 (1) 1975 44-5; PRVW 35; Child III 154-5, and Bronson III 40-46. For broadside editions, see Bodleian, *The Bold Pedlar and Robin Hood*. Such: Harding B 11(382); Catnach: Harding B 11(380), Johnson Ballads 169, and Harding B 11(381). See also *Robin Hood Newly Revived*: Wood 401(27v, 28r) and Douce Ballads 3(120b).]

Rounding The Horn

(FSJ V (19) 1915 165) Roud 301

Mr Bolton, an old sailing ship shantyman, had a remarkably fine repertory of sea-songs (see, for instance, pp. 000 and 000 of this collection). Somewhat to our surprise, we have not found any other published version of *Rounding The Horn*. The song seems to have been rather well-known among nineteenth-century sea-men. Miss Gilchrist collected another version in which the ship is called the *Conway*. In 1793, the crew of a ship called *Amphitrite* addressed a petition to the authorities complaining about the flog-gings ordered by the mate, 'a most Cruel and Barberous man'. The song may be a little later, though it is hard to be sure in these matters. The use of the description 'frigate' would imply that the vessel was a naval one. On the other hand, the ref-erence may be to the brig *Amphitrite*, built in 1820 and engaged in the South American trade. The tune, a mixolydian come-all-ye melody, is a variant of *The Painful Plough*, and of the carol, *Come All You Worthy Christian Men*. It is also used for some sets of the convict transport ballad, *Van Diemen's Land*.

[Roud classifies this under the same heading as *The Loss of the Amphitrite* (Laws K4), a broadside ballad on the wreck off Boulogne of a ship of that name in 1833; it was carrying female convicts. See, for example, Bodleian, Firth c.13(277).

When Anne Gilchrist first noted this song from William Bolton, he remem-bered only the last four verses printed here. He wrote the words down for her without a title (Gilchrist Collection AGG/8/4), at first rendering the first line of verse 4 as 'Whilst beating off the Falkland Isles it blew exceeding hard', but crossing out 'the Falkland Isles' and substituting 'Magellan Strait'. Later, he wrote the song out again (AGG 7/274B), calling it *Rounding the Horn (New version by W Bolton)*; in the meantime he had remembered or reconstructed our verses 1 and 2, and added two more of his own making to go between them:

Next day we weighed our anchor boys, and wav'd good bye all round
And some of us we knew would never more see Plymouth Sound

But still our hearts were light and gay, and when all was taut and snug
We foraged out the bumboat grog and each man filled his mug.

We drank success to Plymouth girls, to Kate and Poll and Sue
And arguing o'er their various charms struck up a fight or two

Jim Crab he landed Bonny Hodge, a clout that made him snort
And to this day his nose has got a heavy list to port!

These stanzas were not used in the *Journal*, however. Miss Gilchrist com-mented 'A hiatus between verses 1 and 2 he had himself supplied, having a chanty-man's gift for verse-making, but as his own verses were less artless than the remainder of this genuine if doggerel production of some sailor bard, I have omitted them, in order to maintain its character.' Roy Palmer (PBC 259-60) quotes the full text and refers to com-ments made by Sam Noble in his book *'Tween Decks in the Seventies* (1925) to the effect that the names of other ports and ships were frequently substituted. It may indeed be the case that it was Mr Bolton who introduced the *Amphitrite* into this song; of the few further examples recorded from tradition, two give the ship's name as the *Conway* (KCSC II 290-1 and an unpublished text, Gilchrist AGG/8/61-62), one as the *Convoy* (PFD 80) and one as the *Comrade* (Richards and Stubbs, *The English Folksinger* 36). A look at notable ships named *Conway*, then, may turn out to be as productive as an examination of *Amphitrites*; as it happens, HMS *Conway*, laid down in 1828, was a sixth rate man of war of 652 tons, with 26 guns; a Jackass Frigate with a full complement of 175 men and boys. She was at Valparaiso in June 1835, and Charles Darwin, about to sail on the *Beagle* for the Galapagos Islands, sent letters and specimens back to England on her (see http://www.hmsconway.org/). A version from Northern Ireland, on the other hand, names the ship as the *Hero* (Gale Huntington, Lani Herrmann and John Moulden, *Sam Henry's Songs of the People*, University of Georgia Press 1990, 97-8).

The Royal Oak

(FSJ V (19) 1915 167) Roud 951

Baring-Gould obtained a version of this song in the West Country [BGSW 226-7]. His singer called it *The Marigold*, and named the captain 'Sir James Merrifield', of Bristol. In a broadside text quoted in Firth's *Naval Songs and Ballads* 87, and also in a version printed by Gavin Greig in his *Folk-Song of the North-East* [also E. B. Lyle and P. Shuldham-Shaw (eds.), *The Greig-Duncan Folk Song Collection*, Aberdeen 1981, I 89], the ship is again the *Marigold*, and its master is given as 'Captain Mansfield of Bristol Town'. Firth suggests that the reference may be to Captain Michael Mansfield, mentioned in Charnock's *Biographia Navalis* I 348, and that the action of the song is

'probably based on Kempthorne's repulse of the seven Algerine ships, December 29, 1669'. The name *Royal Oak* seems to have crept into the song by accident.

[For a broadside text, see *Captain Mansfield's Fight with the Turks at Sea* (PBC 55-7). Another version, *The Good Luck Ship*, was in the repertoire of Harry Cox of Catfield, Norfolk (JEFDSS V (1) 1946 20), and can be heard on Topic Records, *Harry Cox: The Bonny Labouring Boy* (TSCD512D, 2000).]

The Sailor from Dover

(FSJ VIII (31) 1927 5) Roud 180 Laws P9

Child has a ballad called *The Brown Girl* [Child 295, Roud 180] which is like the *Dover Sailor* in reverse, for there it is the man who first scorns the girl, then falls sick with love for her, and the girl arrives and mocks his situation. There is some argument as to whether *The Dover Sailor* is sufficiently distinct to be reckoned as a separate song. The song has not often been reported since Child's time; apart from the present Somerset version, the only other [English] printed set is in KG 20. Both versions seem to derive from the broadside *Sally and her True Love Billy* (issued without imprint). In America, where the song is more common, it is also called *A Brave Irish Lady*. The 'doctor' stanza seems to impress singers deeply; Sharp found an Appalachian version in which the lover actually appears as a physician.

[Mrs Durston's text was a little confused in some places; the editors have modified it, partly with reference to the broadside text mentioned. See, among a number of editions of *Sally* by various printers,

Bodleian, Harding B 15(273b). They have also removed her final two verses:

Rings from her fingers by one, two and three,
'Take these, my dearest William, in remembrance of me,
In remembrance of me, my love, when I am dead and gone,
So perhaps you will be sorry for what you have done.'
'Oh no, my dearest Sally, as long as I've got health
I'll dance all on your grave, my love, as you lie under the earth.
You not pity me ten thousand times over my folly I see.'

An early holograph copy of *The Irish Lady*, made in 1808 by Hannah Lowell on Plum Island, Massachusetts, turned up in an internet auction in November 2002. The song also appeared on broadsides as *The Sailor from Dover*. For a variant with a happy ending, see Bodleian, Harding B 25(1689), *The Sailor from Sunderland*. Beside the two examples of *The Brown Girl* in Child V 166-8, there was another broadside edition titled *The Cruel Nymph: a new song*; this is reprinted in ED&S 63 (1) 2001 10. See also Bronson IV 402-22.]

A Sailor In The North Country

(FSJ II (8) 1906 194) Roud 1504

We have not found any other published set of this song, either in the British collections or those of the North Atlantic seaboard (though it is the kind of song that often found favour among the maritime communities of Newfoundland and Nova Scotia). It appeared not infrequently on nineteenth century broadsides,

though from its graces we presume it is of rather earlier composition. In her rendering of the opening phrase of the song, Mrs Verrall may have had in mind her version of the tune of *Salisbury Plain* (q.v.).

[For a set from George 'Pop' Maynard of Copthorne, Sussex, see JEFDSS 9 (4) 1963 193-4; a recording can be heard on Topic Records, *We've Received Orders to Sail* (TSCD662 1999). A Gloucestershire version appears in KCSC II 554-5.]

A Sailor's Life

(FSJ I (3) 1901 99) Roud 273 Laws K12

This favourite song has an obscure connexion with another popular piece sometimes called *Died For Love* (from which the students' song *There is a Tavern in the Town* has descended) [Roud 60 Laws P25]. Though it lacks the central story of the girl's ocean search for her sweetheart, *Died For Love* has a similar tune, and some versions use the opening stanza of *A Sailor's Life*. In revenge, some sets of *A Sailor's Life* borrow the conclusion of the other song, with the girl directing that her grave be dug wide and deep, and a white turtle dove be put on it, to show that she 'died for love'. In fact, various singers seem to have 'cross-pollenated' the two songs in several ways. Mr Hills' version has the story at once completer and more concisely than usual, and less contaminated with *Died For Love*. In England, the song has also been reported, sometimes under the titles of *Sweet William*, or *Early, Early all in the Spring*, from Lincolnshire (FSJ II (9) 1906 293-4), Dorset (FSJ VIII (34) 1930 212), Worcestershire (BCS 74-5), Somerset (SEF II), and Suffolk (MSS 26-9). Kidson

(KG 92) prints a set of unidentified origin. Pitts and Catnach both published broadsides of the song (the latter called it *The Sailor Boy and his Faithful Mary*). It seems particularly common in the United States, and has been adapted to the life of timber-raftsmen.

[See also FSJ IV (15) 1910 133 (Lancashire, tune and one verse); FMJ 6 (3) 1992 349-50 (Gloucestershire); ED&S 45 (1) 1983 13; PBC 168-9 (Henry Hills); PRVW 141-2 and S100 162-3 (collated from several sources). For broadside editions, see Bodleian, Firth c.12(226) and others: *Sailor boy* (Pitts); Harding B 11(2298): *The maid's lament for her sailor boy* (Catnach); Firth c.12(227): *The sailor boy and his faithful Mary* (Harkness of Preston); Bodleian 2806 b.9(203) and others: *A new song call-l'd the Young lady's lamentation for the loss of her true love* (Brereton of Dublin).]

Salisbury Plain

(FSJ II (8) 1906 196) Roud 1487

The highwayman's 'goodnight' ballad, in which the hero turns robber to support his wife and ends up on the gallows, was a favourite with eighteenth and nineteenth century fairground singers and balladmongers. Such ballads were usually announced as 'the dying testament' of some well-known thief. The present song gains piquancy through being put in the mouth of the robber's sweetheart. The words as given here were obtained by Ralph Vaughan Williams from Mr Henry Burstow of Horsham, Sussex, a neighbour of Mr and Mrs Verrall, whose tune we include. Miss Lucy Broadwood had attempted to notate the song from Mr Burstow in 1893, but he had been too shy to sing her even one line of the words, and in consequence he had only been able to hum and whistle the tune confusedly. The experience, wrote Miss Broadwood, 'proves how impossible it is for country singers to detach tunes from words.' Variants of this melody have wandered all over Europe, seeming to have a common ancestor in the fifteenth century Burgundian basse danse *Le petit roysin* (see W. Wiora, *Europäischer Volksgegang*, Cologne, 1952, p. 50). Five more Sussex versions are in FSJ II (8) 1906 197 and IV (17) 1913 323-4. Miss Broadwood's transcription of Mr Burstow's tune is in FSJ I (4) 1902 150. In the FSJ Index, the song is confused with another, quite distinct, piece called *The Blues* [Roud 588].

[The editors have modified Mr Burstow's text in places, and omitted the final verse:

So now young men a warning take by me,
And never keep those flash girls company,
For if that you do you will rue,
And you will die upon the high drop at last.

For the unaltered text, see PECS 92. Most of the other examples in the *Journal* are tunes without texts, but a set noted by Sharp from Mrs Monnery, Shipley, Sussex, 1908, can be seen in KCSC II 155-6 (tune and text) and in RIP 189-90 (text only); the words are very close to those written out by Henry Burstow.]

The Ship in Distress

(FSJ IV (17) 1913 321) Roud 807

The Portuguese ballad *A Nau Caterineta* and the French ballad *La Courte Paille* tell much the same story. The ship has been long at sea, and food has given out. Lots are drawn to see who shall be eaten, and the captain is left with the shortest straw. The cabin boy offers to be sacrificed in his stead, but begs first to be allowed to keep lookout till the next day. In the nick of time he sees land ('Je vois la tour de Babylone, Barbarie de l'autre côté') and the men are saved. Thackeray burlesqued this song in his *Little Billee*. It is likely that the French ballad gave rise to *The Ship in Distress*, which appeared on nineteenth century broadsides. George Butterworth obtained four versions in Sussex (FSJ IV (17) 1913 320-2) and Sharp printed one from James Bishop of Priddy, Somerset (SFS III 64, KCSC II 297-8 and S100 208, modified) with 'in many respects the grandest air' which he had found in that county. The text comes partly from Mr Bishop's version, and partly from a broadside.

[As indicated, only Mr Harwood's tune appeared in the *Journal*. Most of the text here is from Mr Bishop, with details added from Sharp's partial re-write of it (SFS etc.) and from the broadside reproduced in John Ashton's *Real Sailor Songs* (1891, reprinted London 1973, 44-5). Certain further modifications appear to be wholly editorial; the crewman selected for death is not named in traditional versions of the song, and poetic touches such as 'the great dark water' and 'a full-dressed ship like the sun a-glittering' may well be of Lloyd's own making. See also PBC 165-6; CSB 58-9 and CSES (1971) 210-11 (1997) 145-6, and a (mostly illegible) broadside copy, Bodleian, Harding B 22(357).

Le Petit Navire enjoyed a vogue in the French music halls of the mid-nineteenth century, in a remade version where the luckless cabin boy is indeed eaten, in a variety of interesting sauces. This in turn passed into tradition, mainly as a children's song, alongside its more serious predecessor. Earlier forms of the ballad have been found in Scandinavia; Professor Svend Grundtvig, Child's mentor, published a Danish version of the seventeenth century which also featured Babylon, and in which the mate is butchered and cooked before the crew is miraculously saved, *En Märkelig Vise om de Söfarne Mänd (Folk-Lore Record III* (2) 1881 254-7). For a Brazilian set of *A Nau Caterineta*, see A. L. Lloyd and Isabel Aretz de Ramón y Rivera, *Folk Songs of the Americas* (London: Novello, 1965, 202-3). *La Courte Paille* and its variants appear in many collections of French and French Canadian folk songs; see, for example, Henri Davenson, *Le Livre des Chansons* (Paris: Cahiers du Rhone, 1955, 3rd edn., 327-9).]

Six Dukes Went A-Fishing

(FSJ III (12) 1908 170) Roud 78

To folk-singers, the drowned man in this song is either the Duke of Grantham, or Grafton, or Bedford. Miss Lucy Broadwood suggests (FSJ III (12) 1908 176-9) that he may have been in fact William de la Pole, first Duke of Suffolk who in 1450 was murdered by his political enemies, and his body flung upon the sea-shore at Dover. (Shakespeare writes his version in Henry VI, Part II, Act 4). The 'black was their mourning' stanza occurs also in the ballad of *The Death of Queen Jane*, presumably being borrowed from *Six Dukes* if, as seems probable, the latter is the older song. Other 'borrowings' from this ballad appear in a broad-side of 1690, called *The Noble Funeral of the Renowned Champion the Duke of Grafton who was Slain at the Siege of Cork and Royally Interred in Westminster Abbey. To the tune of, Fond Boy: or, Loves a Sweet Passion. (Printed for Charles Bates at the Sun and Bible in Py-Corner.)* Grainger recorded three versions in Lincolnshire (FSJ III (12) 1908 170-4) and Sharp found one (of Yorkshire origin) in the Marylebone Workhouse, London (FSJ V (18) 1914 79 [and S100 50-1]).

[A few minor modifications have been made. Also quoted in FSJ III are four stanzas of the 1690 broadside and a fur-ther text from tradition, published by the Ballad Society in 1885. A Sussex version appeared in ED&S 29 (4) 1967 112, and two sets from Vermont can be seen in Helen Hartness Flanders, *Ancient Ballads Traditionally Sung in New England*, Philadelphia: University of Pennsylvania, III 1963 159-162. Child printed an incomplete text, *The Duke of Bedford* (Child V 298), taken from *Longman's Magazine*, XVII 1890 217, 'sent from Suffolk'. He considered half of it to be a plagiarism from *The Death of Queen Jane*, and the remainder to be 'so trivial that it is not worth the while at present to assign that piece its own place ... I have not attempted to identify this duke of Bedford; any other duke would probably answer as well.'

The identity of the victim was further discussed in a paper by Mary Rowland, 'Which Noble Duke?' (FMJ I (1) 1965 25-37). She considered a number of can-didates, including de la Pole (the first Duke of Suffolk); Henry Fitzroy, Duke of Grafton (Charles II's son by Barbara Villiers, and subject of the *Noble Funeral*

broadside of 1690); Lord Tavistock, son of the 4th Duke of Bedford, who died in a hunting accident in 1767; Jasper Tudor, Duke of Bedford and Lord Lieutenant of Ireland (died 1495); John Plantagenet, Duke of Bedford and Regent of France (died in 1435, and buried 'betwixt two towers' in Rheims), and George Neville, Duke of Bedford (1457-1483, buried in Yorkshire). She reached no firm conclu-sion, but rather inclined toward the last possibility.]

The Streams of Lovely Nancy

(FSJ VII (27) 1923 59) Roud 688

Our text has been amended and filled out with fragments from various sources, notably from Sussex versions obtained by Miss A. G. Gilchrist, and Francis Jekyll and George Butterworth (FSJ IV (17) 1913 310-11). Even so its meaning is far from clear. W. P. Merrick also reported the song from Sussex (FSJ I (3) 1901 122) as did Lucy Broadwood (BCS 136, under the title *Faithful Emma*). Baring-Gould prints a West Country set in BGSW as *The Streams of Nantsian*. All these, and the broadsides by Catnach, Pitt, and Such, are equally incoherent and mysterious. Miss Broadwood sug-gests that the song originated in Cornwall, and that the 'little streamers that walk the meadows gay' may be young tin-miners, boys or girls, who 'stream' or wash the ore. Both she and Miss Gilchrist (in FSJ IV (17) 1913 312-19) detect traces of an old mystical orig-inal in this curious song. Certain details of its setting are reminiscent of 'The Castle of Love and Grace', a parabolic representation of the Virgin, in the four-teenth century poem, *Cursor Mundi*. Miss

Gilchrist offers persuasive evidence that 'in the *Streamers* we might have an unrecognised relic of a hymn to Mary'.

[Mr Dowden had three verses, two of which appear here in first and third places; the latter a little modified. His third verse – a conflation of two which appear in some broadside versions – was:

As the sailor and his true love was a-walking along,
Said the sailor to his true love: 'I will sing you a song,
It's a falsehearted woman caused my heart for to say
"O! I never will be married, till my love come again!"'

Versions have also been found in Canada, the USA and Ireland. Other examples appear in KCSC II 533-6 and REC 251-3. Broadside editions issued in London, Birmingham, Carlisle, Manchester, Liverpool and York can be seen in the Bodleian collection, among them Firth c.13(24) (Pitts); and Harding B 11(3678) (Such). The Catnach text is quoted in FSJ VII (27) 1923 60. Broadside texts usually include additional verses borrowed from *The Manchester Angel*, q.v. The questions of material shared with a loose group of songs which includes *Bonny Udny* (Roud 3450), *The Boys of Kilkenny* (Roud 1451), *Oh Yarmouth is a Pretty Town* (Roud 1068), *Bonny Portmore* (Roud 3475) and others, and whether or not *The Streams of Lovely Nancy* and *Come All You Little Streamers* should be considered separate, though related, songs, would repay further investigation. Little mention is made in the *Journals* of the obvious erotic symbolism of this song, but sexual imagery was of course by no means uncommon in religious mystical allegory,

if that is indeed what we have here. At all events, the song was popular enough to have spawned a broadside sequel, *Answer to The Streams of Lovely Nancy* (see, for example, Bodleian, Firth c.12(334)), which is a fairly conventional 'sailor meets maiden and marries above his station' story, and not at all mysterious; though perhaps a little dream-like in a fairytale kind of way.]

The Trees They Grow So High

(FSJ II (7) 1905 95) Roud 31 Laws O35

This is one of the most curious, most beautiful, and most widespread of British ballads. Some fifty years ago, Kidson reported it as 'common all over the country', and it is not infrequently met with nowadays, especially in Scotland and Ireland. Sharp alone collected a dozen sets of it. Perhaps the fullest printed texts are Scottish, though English and Irish sets include stanzas not found in Scottish versions. It is sometimes said that the ballad is based on the actual marriage of the juvenile laird of Craigton to a girl several years his senior, the laird dying three years later in 1634. But in fact the ballad may be older; indeed, there is no clear evidence that it is Scottish in origin. Child marriages for the consolidation of family fortunes were not unusual in the Middle Ages and in some parts the custom persisted far into the seventeenth century. The presenting and wearing of coloured ribbons, once common in Britain, still plays a prominent part in betrothal and marriage in Central and Eastern Europe. For some reason this ballad, so common in Britain, is very rare in the U.S.A. The melody given is in the Phrygian mode, seldom met with in English folk song (a different tune to these words, in BGSW 8-9, is also Phrygian). Only one stanza of Miss Bidder's version [the second here] has survived. The greater part of the text we print comes from the versions sung to Sharp by Harry Richards of Curry Rivell, Somerset, in 1904 (FSJ II (6) 1905 44-6 [and S100 58-9, modified]), and to Lucy Broadwood by Mrs Joiner, of Chiswell Green, Hertfordshire, in 1914 (FSJ V (19) 1915 190). In FSJ, further versions will be found from Surrey (I (4) 1904 214-15), Somerset (II (6) 1905 46-7), Sussex (II (8) 1906 206), Yorkshire (II (9) 1906 274), and Dorset (II (9) 1906 275).

[Various small alterations have been made to the introduced material. Verse 5 here is from the set in FSJ I. That verse is not often found in traditional or broadside versions, though Baring-Gould noted a form of it which he removed – for the usual reasons – from the set published in BGSW. It is quoted in REC 265-9 from his MS notes. An early text which also includes it is quoted from Charles Kirkpatrick Sharpe's MSS by David Buchan, *A Book of Scottish Ballads*, Routledge & Kegan Paul, 1973 133-4. Further sets appear in FSJ V (19) 1915 192 (Lancashire) and JEFDSS VI (3) 1951 86-7 (Nova Scotia). See also DPG 44, KFBI 473-4, and PECC 178-80 (Walter Pardon; a recording can be heard on Topic Records TSCD 653, *O'er his Grave the Grass Grew Green*). A broadside text printed by Such was quoted in FSJ II (9) 1906 275-6. For further broadside editions, see, among others, Bodleian, 2806 c.16(80): *My bonny boy is young but he's growing*, and Harding B 11(1685): *My bonny lad is young and growing*.]

The Whale-Catchers

(FSJ I (3) 1901 101) Roud 3291

This song is sometimes confused with the one called *The Greenland Whale Fishery* [under which title it originally appeared in the *Journal*], though in fact the two pieces are separate. From its reference to London, it would seem that *The Whale-Catchers* may once have belonged to the whalemen who sailed out of the Greenland Dock, in Deptford. The version follows the usual pattern of whaling songs – the departure, hard times on the whaling grounds, the rowdy return to port – but it lacks the graphic detail of the chase that distinguishes *The Greenland Whale Fishery*. 'Imez' is written as the singer pronounced it, but we have not traced the whereabouts of this place. This seems to be the only version of the song recovered from oral tradition.

[The repeat of the end lines here is editorial; Mr Hills in fact ended each verse with, 'What cheers your home', pronounced 'what sheers yer 'ome'. He was vague about the meaning, but the carter from whom he had learned it had sung it that way.]

When I Was a Little Boy

(JEFDSS VI (1) 1949 14) Roud 1706

Though this topsy turvy song was collected in the Shetlands, it seems to be English enough to qualify for inclusion here. The suggestion has been made that it is a folk song converted into a comic song for the amusement of London audiences. It belongs to the great family of 'Songs of Marvels' or 'Songs of Lies', along with *The Derby Ram* [Roud 126], *A Shoulder of Mutton Jumped over from France* (FSJ V (20) 1916 292 [Roud 2423]) and, in America, *Nottamun Town* [Roud 1044]. The present song is found in America, entitled *The Little Brown Dog*.

[The editors omit Mr Stickle's third verse:

I bought myself a little dog and the name of him was Don;
So boldly as I trained him to buff and fight and run.
His legs was nine yards long, Sir, his paw was four yards broad,
And around the world in half an hour upon him I could ride.

Dr Gardiner found a version in Hampshire, 1906. The text is printed, as *As I Set Off to Turkey*, in REC 45. Gardiner commented: 'It was current among young people about 1830-40'. A Devon set from the Baring-Gould MSS appeared in ED&S 27 (3) 1964 82. The song has been more widely reported in the USA, Canada, and Scotland, under a variety of names. There is sometimes a giant-killing episode, absent here, which would explain the second half of Mr Stickle's final verse; see, for example, Peacock, *Songs of the Newfoundland Outports*, Ottawa: National Museum of Canada, 1965 I 24-9.]

When I Was Young

(JEFDSS IV (1) 1940 5) Roud 894

The widespread song about the joyful maid who becomes a sorrowful wife would seem to be quite old (in some versions she wears shoes of 'spanish black' and a girdle that sold for a hundred pounds). Possibly its persistence was helped by its inclusion in a popular songster, *120 Comic Songs sung by Sam Cowell*, about 1850. The even wider-known song from the man's point of view, *When I was Single, Oh Then* [Roud 437], presumably

sprang from this. Besides this Durham version, sets have been reported from North Yorkshire (KTT 156), Devonshire (JEFDSS III (1) 1936 51), and 'the West Country' (*Word Lore* Vol. 2, 1927). A version of the male counterblast from Oxfordshire is in WUP 111.

[The singer, Mrs Moore, was originally from Belsay, Northumberland, and had learned this and other songs from her mother. The tune from Sam Cowell's book was reproduced in FSJ VIII (33) 1929 148, together with a text that appeared in Joseph Ritson's *North Country Chorister* (1802). Cowell's first verse, also given, ran:

When I was a maid, O then, O then,
When I was a maid, O then,
As many bright stars as appear in the sky,
So many lovers were caught by my eye,
But I was a beauty then, O then,
But I was a beauty then.

See also Bodleian: Harding B 16(293c), *The Unfortunate Wife*, and Harding B 25(657), *The first wife the best* ('When I was a young man, O then ...'). *Single Girl*, widespread in the USA (Roud 436) and the much rarer *Still I Love Him* (Roud 654; see KFBI 460), share the same theme and many points of detail.]

Ye Mar'ners All

(FSJ III (11) 1907 116) Roud 1191

The raffish words of this song were in print in 1838 or shortly after, in one of a set of miniature penny song-books called *Little Warblers*, published by Ryle of Seven Dials, London. The handsome melody is a variant of a tune used for the well-known *Died for Love*. Barratt prints a

Wiltshire version called *A Jug of This* in BF. Hammond at first understood Mrs Russell to sing 'Ye *mourners* all' but later presumed that she meant 'mariners'. Mrs Russell's words were fragmentary, and Hammond filled out the text from a version supplied by W. Haines 'of Halfway House between Sherborne and Yeovil'.

[Hammond wrote, 'In fact almost all of the words are Haines', Mrs Russell's being fragmentary'. The song appeared on broadsides as (*A*) *Jug of This*; where the uncertain word is indeed 'mariners'. See, for example, Bodleian, Firth c.12(161).]

The Young And Single Sailor

(FSJ IV (15) 1910 128) Roud 264 Laws N42

This is an (eighteenth century?) adaptation of the old half-ring story, widespread in European balladry. It was published on various broadsides, notably by Such, and appears in *The Vocal Library* songbook published in London in 1822. The well-known *Fair Phoebe and her Dark Eyed Sailor*, probably a stage song of the 1830s, derives from this ballad, which is also reported from oral tradition in Hampshire (FSJ IV (15) 1910 127), Herefordshire (FSJ IV (15) 1910 128), Dorset and Sussex (FSJ IV (15) 1910 129), and Somerset (SFS II 40). FSJ VI (25) 1922 272-3 offers an Irish version.

[Only Mr Burridge's (or Burrage's) tune was published in the *Journal*, RVW having noted no words from him. The editors have collated two texts here; one from Mrs Vaisey, Adwell, Oxfordshire, noted by Lucy Broadwood in September 1892 (the 'Hampshire' version referred to above; Mrs Vaisey was a native of that county) and one from Mr Conny Cochlan, Derrynasaggart, County Cork,

noted by A. Martin Freeman (the Irish version cited, anglicised to a degree here). They have also made some small changes of their own. Further sets appear in FMJ 5 (3) 1987 353-5 (Yorkshire); PMB 29 (Dorset); REC 64-5 (Hampshire), and SLM 88-9 (Sussex). A broadside facsimile appears in ED&S 32 (3) 1970 103.

A widespread song, popular in Britain, Ireland, the USA and Canada, and still to be found in tradition. For the Such broadside, see Bodleian, Firth c.12(335): *Young and Single Sailor*. Other examples appear as *The Loyal Sailor* and *The Sailor's Return*.]

Young Edwin in the Lowlands Low

(FSJ III (13) 1909 266) Roud 182 Laws M34

This ballad was evidently a great favourite, for versions of it were printed on balladsheets by many printers in England, Scotland and Ireland. Several versions have been found in the Northeast and the upland South of America. The hero is variously given as Young Edwin, Young Edward, and Young Edmund. Mrs Hopkins's tune is sometimes used for the carol, *Come All You Worthy Christians* (e.g. FSJ I (3) 1901 74). It appears to be related to the well-known *Dives and Lazarus* melody (perhaps both are descended from a common ancestor). Other English versions have been reported from oral tradition in Sussex (FSJ I (3) 1901 124), and Hampshire (GFH 38). A Canadian set collected by Maud Karpeles is given in FSJ VIII (34) 1930 227-8.

[Beside various small modifications to the text as it appeared in the *Journal*, the editors have partly rewritten verses 2, 3,

4 and 5, and changed the line order of verse 8. The penultimate verse here is conflated from two:

Says Emma, 'I will wander down by the stormy seas,
Where Edwin he lies under who once did brave the breeze.
The shells that in the ocean are rolling to and fro
Reminds me of my Edwin that ploughed the Lowlands Low.'

'The fishes of the ocean swim o'er my lover's breast.
His body rolls in motion, I hope his soul's at rest.
How cruel was my parents to prove his overthrow,
And take the gold from one so bold that ploughed the Lowlands Low.'

Mrs Hopkins was 25 when George Gardiner and Charles Gamblin noted the song from her. In his notes to the Gardiner MS collection (Item H.998), Frank Purslow points out that the text printed in the *Journal* didn't come from her at all, but from a Mr Clark of Ropley (H.115). Only two verses were noted from Mrs Hopkins:

Young Emma was a servant maid
She loved a sailor bold
He ploughed the main much gold to gain
For her love as we are told.

'I'll meet you in the morning
Do not let my parents know
That how I love young Edwin
That ploughed the Lowlands Low.'

See also PMB 101 (Dorset). The song appeared on broadsides as *Young Edmund* (or *Edwin*) *in the Lowlands Low*, and a number of examples can be seen at the Bodleian collection. For more on the history of the tune, see Simpson, *The British Broadside Ballad and Its Music,* 109 and 252-4.]

The Young Girl Cut Down In Her Prime

(FSJ IV (17) 1913 325) Roud 2 Laws Q26/B1

At the end of the eighteenth century a homilectic street ballad spread in England concerning the death and ceremonial funeral of a soldier 'disordered' by a woman. It was called *The Unfortunate Rake* (in Ireland) or *The Unfortunate Lad* (on the broadside printed by Such). Many singers know it as *St James's Hospital*. It is still a common song in the British Army, though printed versions are few. English sets have been reported from Yorkshire (FSJ I (5) 1904 254) and Hampshire (FSJ III (13) 1909 292). Our song represents a later development, in which the sexes are reversed, but the ceremonial funeral is retained. Versions of this form have been recorded from Oxfordshire and Somerset as well as the present Hampshire version. In America, the song has been adapted to the cattle range (*The Cowboy's Lament* or *The Streets of Laredo*) and the gambling hall (*St James' Infirmary*). The motif of the ceremonial funeral remains constant, despite all the transformations of the chief character.

[The editors have polished the text as it appeared in the *Journal*. The singer repeated the final verse given here after verses 4 and 5 and her own final verse, which has been omitted:

And when I am dead, to the church they will carry me,
Six pretty maidens to bear up my pall,
And in each of their hands a bunch of

primroses,
Saying, 'there goes a true-hearted girl to her home.'

Also given were two other tunes noted by Cecil Sharp in Oxfordshire and Somerset, each accompanied by a single verse only; one with a female, the other with a male protagonist.

A further *Young Girl* set sung by Mrs Joiner (source of *The Bramble Briar* in this book), appeared in FSJ V (19) 1915 193-4. The second 'Hampshire set' referred to above is actually a completely different song, *The Lass of London City* (*White Copper Alley*) (Roud 1554), though sung to an *Unfortunate Rake* tune variant (see also PWS 66). Versions have been found in the USA and Canada as *The Bad Girl's Lament*. Broadside examples of *The Unfortunate Lad* can be seen at the Bodleian collection. See also *Root and Branch I*, *A New World*, for a brief examination by David Atkinson of the various branches of this song-family.]

A. L. Lloyd recorded many of the songs in this book on the *Collector* LP JGB 5001, 1960, and on an EP, *Collector* JEB 8. These have now been reissued on CD by Fellside Records of Cumbria, as *A. L. Lloyd: England & Her Traditional Songs* (Fellside FECD 173, 2003). Fellside also has a compilation of recordings by various revival singers, *A Selection from the Penguin Book of English Folk Songs* (FECD47).

A range of recordings of traditional singers is available from Folktrax (including all the examples quoted in Kennedy's *Folksongs of Britain and Ireland*); Musical Traditions; Topic Records (in particular, their extensive *Voice of the People* series), and Veteran. Details are in the bibliography. Transcriptions of cylinder recordings made by Grainger and by Vaughan Williams are held at the Vaughan Williams Memorial Library.

THE SINGERS

The folk song collectors of the early part of the twentieth century were for the most part enthusiastic amateurs. Some, like Cecil Sharp and the Hammond brothers, amassed large bodies of material, while others just picked up the occasional song when an opportunity presented itself. Some brought considerable scholarship to bear upon their work, while others preferred to leave that side of things to specialists like Frank Kidson, Lucy Broadwood or Anne Gilchrist. The full spectrum is represented here. The extent to which collectors felt it important to record details of their sources varied a great deal, and, even where they did keep substantive information, it often did not appear in the *Journals*: the Folk Song Society was primarily interested in the songs, and most particularly in their tunes.

A far greater emphasis is placed today upon context, and folk song is seen as just one part of a larger cultural phenomenon, encompassing not only other areas of a singer's repertoire (many of those represented here also knew a lot of popular songs of the day, for example; some made a distinction between them and their 'old' songs, while others did not) but also other aspects of tradition which they carry, and the place these cultural artefacts occupy in their lives and in that of the surrounding community.

With that in mind, some information on the singers represented in this book is included here. In some cases, little or none is to be found; few wrote about themselves as did Henry Burstow or William Bolton. However, there is useful information in some of the original manuscript collections, and material from the censuses of 1901 and 1881 is available online, principally via the websites of the Public Records Office and the Church of Jesus Christ of Latter-day Saints, though it should be remembered that tran scribed data – and, indeed, the original records – are not always accurate. Some identifications, though likely, are not certain. Printed and other sources have also been used; these are detailed below, together with references to other material noted from the singers.

These short pieces are not intended to be comprehensive or definitive, but to show the reader a little of the personal and social contexts from which the songs in this book were gathered. A lot more research might usefully be done. In a few cases (Burstow and Bolton in particular), only a short summary of available information is given, and some of Sharp's singers mentioned here are dealt with in greater detail in EFDSS' recent publication *Still Growing,* drawing on the researches of Bob and Jacqueline Patten, Dave Bland, Keith Chandler and others.

W. Alexander

George Gardiner and (probably) Charles Gamblin noted *On Monday Morning* in (probably) 1907, noting that Mr Alexander was 73. The 1901 census shows a William Alexander (67), a shepherd, living at Church Lane, Cliddesden, with his unmarried sons George (36) and Henry (29), both general labourers.

References:

FSJ III (13) 1909 315-6. Gardiner Collection (Vaughan Williams Memorial Library) H1073.

Benjamin Arnold

This may be Benjamin Arnold, licensed victualler of Easton. In the 1881 census he appears as an agricultural labourer and licensed victualler (48), living with his wife Miriam (45) at Main Road North (Prince Of Wales), Holybourne. In 1901 he and Miriam are running the Chestnut Horse Inn at Easton.

References:

FSJ III (13) 1909 253, 255, 278-82, 313-14. PMB 78. PWS 48-9. REC 60-1.

Gardiner Collection H627, H639 and others.

Ann Aston

Ann Aston (née Howell) was born in 1832 at Coleford, Gloucestershire, the daughter of George Howell (a coal miner, later a postman) and Eliza Howell (née Jones). In 1854 she married Edward Aston, a bootmaker. They emigrated to Australia in 1855 on the *John Banks*, settling briefly in South Australia, where their first daughter, Elizabeth, was born. The following year they moved to Victoria. After her husband became ill, Ann Aston worked as a midwife. She died in 1913; Edward had died in 1881. Their daughter, Matilda Ann (Tilly), was born in 1873, the youngest of 7 or 8 children. She was visually impaired from birth, and totally blind by the age of 7. The first blind Australian to go to university (at Melbourne), she was unable to complete the course due to the lack of textbooks in Braille. In 1911 she sent Braille notation of her mother's song to W. P. Merrick, who was himself partially-sighted and had a wide circle of Braille correspondents. Tilly founded the Victorian Association of Braille Writers (later the Vision Australia Library) and the Association for the Advancement of the Blind (later the Vision Australia Foundation), which was instrumental in gaining voting rights for blind people; she was also Head of the School for the Blind in Victoria. She published a number of books of poetry and memoirs, and died in 1947. An electoral district of Melbourne is named after her.

References:

JEFDSS I (1) 1932 52. Broadwood Collection (Vaughan Williams Memorial Library) LEB/5/339.

Vision Australia Foundation: http://www.visionaustralia.org.au/

Chris O'Sullivan, *The Howell Family*: http://home.iprimus.com.au/raccos/

Ted Baines

An agricultural labourer, aged 'about 70' in 1904 when RVW met him at Plummers Plain, Lower Beeding. Edwin Baines (54), an agricultural labourer living at Long Tail Cottage, Lower Beeding, with his wife Rebecca (60) and son William (20; also an agricultural labourer) appears in the 1881 census, but not, apparently, in 1901; though a William Baines (40), beerhouse keeper and bricklayer, is listed at the Wheatshief *(sic)* Inn, Lower Beeding, where he lives with his wife and children.

References:

FSJ II (8) 1906 202-3. PRVW 148-50. Vaughan Williams MSS (Vaughan Williams Memorial Library) II 351, 352, 354.

Mr Baker

Mr Baker spent his whole working life as an engineer at Thomas Tillings'. He was in his seventies when Francis M. Collinson noted *Death and the Lady* from him, and his singing voice was no longer strong; Collinson had to ask him to repeat the tune several times. Collinson also noted three songs from Mrs Baker, who was born at Mereworth, Kent, and had learned them from her father, who knew some 150 songs.

References:

JEFDSS V (1) 1946 19.

Francis Collinson and Francis Dillon, *Folk Songs from Country Magazine*. London, 1952 3-7.

Allan Bates

For references, see notes, *DroylsdenWakes*.

William Bolton

William Bolton was born on 19 May 1840, at Prestwich, Manchester. He joined the Royal Navy in 1852 (pretending to be 14, then the minimum entry age) and served on HMS *Liffey*, and later HMS *Cornwallis*, during the Crimean War. He left the RN in 1863, having spent the previous two years in the storeroom/armoury, and in 1873, after a time working in prisons and as a policeman (in 1878 he published a small book, *Recollections of a Police Officer relating to Dogs, with useful hints as to their treatment in health and disease, etc.*), opened a gunsmith/ship chandler's shop in Southport. It seems that he continued occasionally to go to sea on merchant ships, leaving his wife Mary (with whom he had four children) to run the shop, but his maritime adventures had probably ended by 1888. He was an inveterate storyteller, however, and in a series of autobiographical pieces in the *Southport Advertiser* (1890) he wrote of being shanghaied by a pirate ship (the *Octopus*) while in Bermuda, and of his shoot-out with the outlaw Black Pete while working on a ranch near Calgary.

Mary died in 1896, but William soon remarried, and had two more children with his new wife Carolyne Mary. He was a keen versifier, and his poems (often in acrostic form) appeared in a number of publications. In 1906, he issued a broadside song of his own making, *The Seashore Cot*, to the tune of the *Village Blacksmith* – 'minimum price one penny' – to raise money for the Southport Lifeboat Widows and Orphans Fund. Between 1905 and 1907 he supplied Anne Gilchrist with 17 songs, some of which he censored as they were not, in his opinion, suitable for a lady. Whether or not he had been, as he said, a shantyman, he certainly understood the idiom and looked the part; a photograph taken in 1913 shows him being presented, as a Crimean War veteran, to George V; though stooping rather, he is still a big man (he had been 5 feet 8 inches tall at the age of 12), a head taller than the king. He is dressed for the occasion in his white sailor's jacket and collar. William died on 3 July 1918, but was still remembered locally more than 60 years later; a genuinely larger-than-life character.

References:

Most of the above information is from Frank Sellors, 'William Bolton', ED&S 48 (1) 1986 30-1.

Mike Yates, 'The Best Bar in the Capstan: William Bolton, Sailor and Chantyman'. *Traditional Music* no.7, 10-11.

FSJ II (9) 1906 236-49; FSJ III (10) 1907/8 57-8; FSJ V (19) 1915 165-7. Bronson IV 286.35. PBC 194-6, 204-5, 259-60.

Gilchrist Collection (Vaughan Williams Memorial Library) AGG/7/269-274; AGG/8/20, 46, 57, 60, 62.

Mrs Bowring

The 1901 census shows only one Mrs Bowring at Cerne Abbas: Edith, a widowed tailoress, aged 73. In 1881 she is listed living at 17 Acreman Street with husband Thomas (51), a road labourer; daughters Jane (24), also a tailoress, and Mary Ann (19), a dressmaker; and a granddaughter, Annie Fox (9 months). In 1901 she is still at the same address, as is Jane, unmarried; they are both working from home. There is also another daughter, Annie Hook (38; presumably Mary Ann), and her daughter Lilian Hook (5); and a granddaughter, Evelyn Bowring (15).

References:

FSJ III (11) 1907 28. Hammond Collection (Vaughan Williams Memorial Library) D878-886. Bronson I 20.16; IV 283.7.

Mr Burrage

Spelled 'Burridge' in the *Journal*, but 'Burrage' in RVW's MSS. There are no Burridges listed at Capel in the 1901 census, and the only adult male Burrage listed is John (50), a farm labourer, living at Phills, Capel, with his wife Mary (47), and their son George (9). John and Mary were both born in the Horsham area, but George was born in the Isle of Wight. 'Rushetts', the address at which RVW met Mr Burrage, was at this time occupied by others.

References:

FSJ IV (15) 1910 128. PECS 28-9. Bronson IV (Addenda) 11.1. Vaughan Williams MSS I 252, 254(1,2), 256, 258.

Henry Burstow

Henry Burstow was born on 11 December 1826, the next-youngest of nine. His father, William, was a tobacco-pipe maker, and Henry grew up in 'The Bishopric', Horsham, the roughest part of town. In 1840 he was apprenticed to boot and shoe maker Jim Vaughan; the industry was important locally, and its practitioners had a certain reputation for drinking: 'Ah!' remarked his mother's friends, 'Harry's done for now!' He did indeed spend a lot of time in taprooms over the years, but reckoned to have been drunk only once, when his brandy was spiked at a friend's wedding. His own wedding, to Elizabeth Pratt in 1855, was a more sober affair. Henry's passions were singing and bellringing, and he achieved some local renown in both pursuits. His politics tended to Radicalism, and he was both an atheist and an admirer of Darwin; bellringing was a social and intellectual activity for him (he taught change-ringing to a good many people over the years) rather than a spiritual one.

Singing had always been part of his life. He learned his first song, *Travel the Country Round* (Roud 1067), from his father (who knew nearly 200, 84 of which Henry learned), and subsequently got songs from a great many sources, both oral and printed. He was prepared to go to some lengths to obtain a song he wanted; when a certain carter kept refusing to sing for him because he thought that Henry wanted to laugh at his strong accent, he arranged for a friend to lure the man into an alehouse where, in time, he sang his favourite 'ballet'. Henry was hiding in the next room, and learned it on the spot.

In 1911 he had 420 songs in all, and listed them. On occasion he had sung them all through in sequence; the last time he did that was to mark his wife's 78th birthday. In instalments of ten or so, it took him 41 evenings. In 1893, Lucy Broadwood noted a large number from him, though not without the occasional difficulty; he was adamant, for instance, that *Salisbury Plain* and *Rosemary Lane* were unsuitable for a lady's ears. Henry was pleased to see his songs in print, and 'amazed beyond expression' when Vaughan Williams recorded him on a phonograph some years later and played him the results. Other collectors also visited him; he was the most important singer encountered by the first folk song revival, not just because he was a considerable singer, but because he has left us a complete picture of his repertoire, unfiltered by collectors who were looking for a particular kind of material and were not as a rule interested in recording popular 'composed' songs.

Towards the end of his life, Henry, by then living at 28 Spencer's Road, found himself in considerably straitened circumstances. His friend William Albery put together a book of Henry's memoirs, and this was published by subscription with a view to providing him with funds for his remaining years. He died in January 1916.

References:

Henry Burstow (as told to William Albery), *Reminiscences of Horsham*. Horsham: Free Christian Church Book Society, 1911.

FSJ I (4) 1902 139, 142-177, 208, 210-11. FSJ II (7) 1905 89-90, 192. FSJ II (8) 1906 186-93. FSJ IV (17) 324.

Bronson III 132.11, 209.45; IV 250.21, 278.1. BTSC 2-37, 40-9, 100-7, 113-5. ED&S 39 (3) 1977 102. PBB 119-21. PBC 162-3, 187-8. PECS 35-6, 85-7,117-18. PRVW 168-76.

Broadwood Collection LEB/2/5-23. Vaughan Williams MSS I 403; II 260, 318, 320, 322, 326-337; III 277, 279, 281, 283, 285, 287; 4to I 10-17. Scrapbook: several song texts in Burstow's own hand.

John Collinson

A blacksmith and farmer of Casterton, Westmorland, Collinson was 43 when he won first prize in the folk song category at the Westmorland Musical Festival in May 1905, with *The Wa'ney Cockfeightin' Sang*; Cecil Sharp was the adjudicator. The 'unpublished Country Dialect Song' was quite a new category, and at the 1904 festival Mr Collinson, apparently a late entrant (his name didn't appear in the printed programme) had sung *I Wonder What has Kept My Love* (Roud 2499/858), *Billy Taylor* (Roud 158 Laws N11) and *In Yon Land* (probably Roud 542), for which last he won third prize. Perhaps he took to heart the judge, Frank Kidson's, comments that his other two songs were not very unusual, for he walked all the way to Hutton Roof in order to learn the *Cockfeightin' Sang* from his father-in-law, a noted cock-fighter in his time. It took the older man three days to remember the song, and Mr Collinson commented wryly that it cost him more in lost earnings than the value of the prize he won with it. The following year he sang *The Thresherman* (Roud 19) and *Jack the Sailor* (Roud 1454), but we don't know if he won anything that time. He evidently took care to learn songs just as the older men sang them, but this was not always easy. One elderly singer from whom he was trying to learn a song called *Hoo happy we lived then*, lost patience with him: 'If thoo can't get intult, do wi'oot! – and awa' wi' ye hame!' He got it in the end, though, and sang it at the 1905 festival. Percy Grainger also noted 11 songs from him.

References:

FSJ II (7) 1905 84-5; FSJ V (19)1915 200-1. PECS 204-5.

Broadwood Collection LEB/5/170, 171. Gilchrist Collection AGG/4/53-4 (1904 Festival); AGG/8/25, 33, 36, 37, 39, 51, 70. Grainger MS Collection (hektograph copies, Vaughan Williams Memorial Library), listed in Jane O'Brien, *Grainger's English Folk Song Collection*, University of Western Australia, 1985: ONS 32-42 / RNS 18-28.

Sharp Collection (Vaughan Williams Memorial Library): Folk Tunes 517.

Thomas Coomber

Thomas Marshall Coomber was born in 1865 at Fordcombe, Kent, the second youngest of ten; his father, Richard, worked as a quarryman and, later, as a bricklayer's labourer. Thomas left school early (at the age of 8, he said) and in the 1881 census he is listed as an agricultural labourer, aged 15. On Christmas Day 1884 he married Elizabeth Gasson of Colestock; it was probably the only day they could both get off work. Their first son, also Thomas, had been born the previous May. Thomas got a job on the Railway construction project at Blackham, subsequently moving there to work on Willetts farm as a dairyman. He and Elizabeth lived at Willetts Cottages for the rest of their lives. In later years he also worked as a gardener in order to save up for a good tombstone, and in his spare time he kept dogs and birds. Elizabeth worked as a midwife and layer-out, took in washing and picked hops in the season.

Anne Gilchrist seems first to have met their daughter Florrie, then aged about 14, in 1905; she sang part of *The Squire and the Milkmaid* (*Blackberry Fold*: Roud 559 Laws O10), which she had learned from her mother (who had got it 'out of a song book'). Over the next couple of years, Miss Gilchrist noted a number of songs from the family. Beside *The Gentleman Soldier*, Thomas also sang such songs as *Green Bushes* (Roud 1040 Laws P2), *I Prithee Love Let Me In* (Roud 608), *Barbary Ellen* (Roud 54 Child 84), and – evidently a family favourite – *The Farmer's Life* (Roud 16897), which he had learned from his grandfather. Elizabeth had songs like *The Banks of Sweet Dundee* (Roud 148 Laws M25), *The Undaunted Female* (Roud 289 Laws L3), and *The Folkestone Murder* (Roud 897). She reputedly knew the rather risqué song *The Molecatcher* (Roud 1052). Thomas and Elizabeth also sang songs together, and on occasion the 'Misses Coomber' (Florrie, Beattie, and perhaps also Dorrie, the youngest girl) would also join in (*Fair Phoebe and Her Dark-Eyed Sailor*: Roud 265 Laws N35). Miss Gilchrist also noted a few songs from a Mr Gasson, aged 73; this may have been Elizabeth's father, Humphrey, who lived quite near.

Thomas was described by his grandson, John (Florrie's son), as 'a tall, upright man with pale blue eyes and a large moustache' who habitually wore a scarf tucked into his braces. Elizabeth was about 5 feet 2, ruddy-faced and well built. Thomas died in January 1945 after a short illness; within two months, Elizabeth was also dead.

Most of the biographical information is from Richard Coomber's research on the Coomber and Gasson families. Website: http://www.coomber-family-tree.com/

Other references:

FSJ IV (15) 1910 133; FSJ V (19) 1915 138-9, 156-7, 162, 199; FSJ VI (21) 1918 19-20; FSJ VIII (33) 1929 112.

PECS 90-2. Gilchrist Collection AGG/3/6- 9, 12-19, 22, 39. AGG/8/18, 22, 24, 27, 49-50, 69, 71, 76-7.

Cecilia Costello

Mrs Costello (née Kelly) was 65 when Patrick Shuldham-Shaw and Marie Slocombe recorded her for the BBC at the instigation of her son. Her mother was from County Galway and her father, from whom she learned most of her songs, was from Ballinasloe, County Roscommon. They had moved early to North Shields; Cecilia herself was born in England and spent nearly all her life in Birmingham. Though not fully recovered from a recent illness, she sang for nearly three hours for the BBC (thirteen songs and fragments in all), with a window ajar onto the November fog outside so as to admit a microphone cable from the recording car. Beside the two songs in this book, JEFDSS also printed her versions of *Maid That's Deep in Love* (Roud 231 Laws N12), *The Cruel Mother* (Roud 9 Child 20), *The Jew's Garden* (Roud 73 Child 156), *My Johnny* (Roud 1422: a traditional predecessor of *My Bonny Lies Over the Ocean*), and *The Frog and the Mouse* (Roud 16). Marie Slocombe later wrote:

'*The Cruel Mother* proved to be a particularly fine and complete version. The singer remembered very vividly her father's singing of this ballad. "He sang it", she told us, "with his eyes closed, hands clasped, bending over – with great emphasis and drama, very slow – he used to frighten us children with it". I think that during our recording she was recapturing the way he sang it.'

Mrs Costello was also recorded by Peter Kennedy and by Roy Palmer. Copies of the BBC recordings are held at the Vaughan Williams Memorial Library, and Peter Kennedy's recordings are available from Folktrax (see bibliography).

References:

JEFDSS VII (2) 1953 96-105.

Bronson III 155.55; IV 248.16. Roy Palmer, *Songs of the Midlands*. Wakefield: EP Publishing Ltd, 1972. 33, (reprinted in ED&S 34 (1) 1972 21), 36, 43, 91, 100. KFBI 302. PBB 185-7. BBC recordings 17031-4 and 19929.

Charlotte Dann

Charlotte Few worked as a maid for Ella Bull's family between 1876 and 1877. She was born in 1856 in nearby Willingham, and settled at Cottenham, marrying James Graves Dann, an agricultural labourer one or two years her junior; their first child, Annie, was born in *c.*1880. Miss Bull noted a number of songs from her, probably in 1904, several of which were in 5/4 time. This puzzled her, so she asked W. P. Merrick for advice, and he put her in touch with Lucy Broadwood. Charlotte had learned some of her songs from her mother Anna, who was from nearby Over, but didn't recall where she had picked up *Lucy Wan*. In the 1901 census, James and Charlotte are living at High Street, Cottenham, with their sons Henry (16, an agricultural labourer), George (14, a cycle fitter), Reuben (9) and Ernest (6). Ernest died in the Great War in 1917, aged 22.

References:

JEFDSS I (1) 1932 53-4. Bronson I 51.3. Broadwood Collection LEB/5/62-74.

William Davey

The Hammond brothers met Mr Davy (or Davey) at the Beaminster workhouse in 1906; he was a native of Hook(e). The 1901 census shows a William Davey (67), born in Hook, living at 'Cottage, Cattistock' on parish pay (a locally administered subsistence allowance for the poor). His wife Annie is 36, and they have four sons: Bertie (14), a ploughboy, Frank (7), Fred (3), and Reginald ('under 7 months'); and a daughter, Blanche (10). If, as seems likely, this is the same man, then he must have been obliged through continuing infirmity or unemployment to enter the workhouse; the Poor Law regime of the day would not have permitted the family to stay together. Tragedies of this kind were all too common. Henry Hammond's notes on the two versions of *Gaol Song* mention that 'Davy's gaol-bird is miserable and sings to an appropriately weird tune, whilst [Sam] Gregory's is a humorous fellow, who sings in the major key'. In the circumstances, it is tempting to see a reason for this in the singer's own life.

References:

FSJ VII (27) 1923 47-9. PMB 92. Hammond Collection D482.

Mrs Davis

References:

FSJ III (11) 1907 122-5. Bronson III 209.21; IV (Addenda) 105.27.1. PCL 90. Hammond Collection D704-8.

George Dowden

References:

FSJ VII (27) 1923 87-8. 59, 87. FSJ VIII (34) 1930 196-7.

PCL 66. PFD 16-17, 89. REC 68. Broadwood Collection LEB/5/187. Hammond Collection D198-215.

Lucy Durston

In the 1901 census there are 39 Durstons around Bridgwater. The only Lucy is listed as 48, living with her husband John (41), a self-employed chimney sweep and fire brigade member, at No 3 Court, Albert Street. They have a son, John (6). Apart from *The Sailor From Dover*, Sharp noted a further three tunes from Lucy, but without words. He recorded her age in 1909 as 60, so there is a discrepancy, but this is not unusual.

References:

FSJ VIII (31) 1927 5-6. Bronson IV 295.10. KCSC I 218-9, 647.

Sharp Collection: Folk Tunes 2180-3. Folk Words 2035-6.

Sister Emma

Sister Emma was an Anglican nun at the Community of St John the Baptist at Clewer, near Windsor. The order was founded in 1849 and specialised in helping 'fallen women' to begin with, but rapidly grew to include orphanages, elementary and high schools and colleges, hospitals and mission work. The community also had establishments in India and the USA. The Sisters were described as 'Ladies of the Church of England', many having coming from privileged and even aristocratic families. A Sister Emma was involved in running the St Augustine's Home for Boys at Clewer and, in 1893, during a smallpox epidemic, evacuated the school so that it could be used as a hospital. Though it is likely that this was our Sister Emma, we have no certain information. She gave Sharp some 26 songs in February and March, 1909, including several 'Child' ballads and some Northern English songs such as *Gang o'er the Burn My Canny Hinny* (Roud 13282) and *The Bonnie Pit Laddie* (Roud 3487), learned in childhood from her mother and nurse, sixty or more years previously.

References:

FSJ V (18) 81-2.

Bronson II 73.116, 85.39, 93.28; III 155.25, 200.90; IV 289.38. KCSC I 75-6, 81-2, 106-7, 116-7, 154-5, 170, 216-7. KCSC II 33, 379, 396, 589-90. RIP 69, 74, 102-3, 230.

Sharp Collection: Folk Tunes 2078-90, 2095-2100. Folk Words 1928-58, 1971-6.

Clewer Village website:
http://www.clewer.myby.co.uk/

John Farr

The 1881 census shows John Farr, ship carpenter, aged 31, living at 17 Church Town, Gwithian, Cornwall, with his wife Mary, 24, daughter Phillipa, 7, and son Augustus, 6. He is listed as a carpenter in 1901, living with Mary at 'Lyhthouse Villa'. Phillipa has moved out but is listed as living locally.

References:

FSJ VIII 1928 97-100; reprinted in Inglis Gundry, *Canow Kernow* 1966 39-41.

Agnes Ford

In the 1901 census, Agnes J Ford, 42, is living with her husband William, a blacksmith, at 1, Forge Cottage, at Blackham in the civil parish of Withyham, Sussex. They were both born in Kent; she at Cowden, he at Penshurst. They have a son, William (12) and a daughter, Ethel (8), both also born in Kent, so the family may be fairly new to the area. Anne Gilchrist seems first to have met Ethel, then about 13, who sang her *The Cottage in the Wood* (Roud 608) and *The Farmer's Boy* (Roud 408 Laws Q30), which she had learned from her father. Miss Gilchrist subsequently noted a number of songs from the family, including *Mother Mother Make My Bed* (q.v.) and *The Golden Glove* (Roud 141 Laws N20) from Agnes, who had learned songs from her mother, and *Barbary Ellen* (Roud 54 Child 84) and *Sylvie* (Roud 7 Laws N21) from William, who had got the latter as a boy from his 'mother-in-law' (that is, step-mother). Miss Gilchrist was particularly impressed with William's vigorous and rhythmic singing, and naturally asked whether he sang at his work in the forge; it turned out, though, that he didn't. He was quite in demand at village concerts for one particular song, *The Old Grey Mare* (*The Country Carrier*, Roud 1400) which he had learned 'off a ballad-sheet' and for which he had made up his own tune, which he used to perform 'with dramatic action'.

References:

FSJ VI (21) 1918 21, 31; FSJ VIII (34) 1930 227.

Gilchrist Collection AGG/3/6, 7, 10, 15, 21; AGG/8/6, 16, 28, 32, 48.

Sarah Foster

For references, see notes, *Benjamin Bowmaneer*.

Ted Goffin

E. J. Moeran found a lot of singers around Catfield and Sutton in Norfolk, the best known of whom is Harry Cox. The Goffins have long been connected with the area, and are related to the Larners. Ted's nickname was 'Crip'.

References:

Christopher Heppa, 'Harry Cox's Friends & Fellow Singers' in booklet accompanying Topic Records TSCD512D, 2000, pp. 28-30.

FSJ VII (26) 1922 2-3, 14. Bronson II 57.10 (appendix).

George Gouldthorpe

George Gouldthorpe (Goldthorpe, Goulthorpe) was born *c.*1839 at Barrow-on-Humber, North Lincolnshire, and was 68 when Grainger met him at Glanford Brigg Union Workhouse. He had worked as a lime-burner, and Grainger describes him as an unworldly man of exceptional dignity, though suffering want and hardship after a life of drudgery, with a 'gaunt and sharp-cornered' face and figure and a 'somewhat grating' singing voice, but who 'yet contrives to breathe a spirit of almost caressing tenderness into all he does, says, or sings; even if a hint of tragic undercurrent be present also … His personality, looks, and art are a curious blend of sweetness and grim pathos.' Unlike many Lincolnshire singers, he used little decoration. 'He gives out his tunes in all possible gauntness and barrenness, for the most part in broad, even notes; eschewing the rhythmic contrasts, ornaments, twiddles, slides, and added syllables that most North Lincolnshire singers revel in. His charm lies in the simplicity of his versions, and the richness of his dialect, which he does not eliminate from his songs to the extent that most singers do, while in his everyday speech it might be hard to beat.' He and his brother William, whose style was very similar, had learned their songs in childhood from their father, who was 'much remembered as a great songster'.

The workhouse administrators regularly sent him out to work on the roads, only for him to be sent straight back again when it became clear that he was no longer strong enough for manual labour; he seems to have borne this pointless indignity with stoicism and good humour. His 'mild yet lordly grandeur' was the inspiration for Grainger's setting of *Horkstow Grange* (Roud 1760), another of his songs.

Grainger encouraged his singers to enter the folk song competition at Brigg, and in 1906 Mr Gouldthorpe sang *Six Dukes* there. Lucy Broadwood later wrote:

'Mr Gouldthorpe's fifth and sixth verses appeared with dramatic suddenness. He had many times sung the song without them, asserting that the ballad was complete. The excitement of singing in the folk song competition at Brigg must have set his sub-conscious memory to work, and on the concert platform he quite naturally included the forgotten stanzas, to his own utter amazement, for he had not thought of them for forty years, he was sure!'

References:

Programme notes, *Lincolnshire Posy*, 1939.

FSJ III (12) 1908 164-5, 170-3, 214-8. FMJ 2 (5) 1974 338-40. Bronson II 75.52; IV 279.30. SYB I 13-14, 35-6, 51-2.

Grainger MS Collection 103, 108, 135, 139, 140, 178, 190, 199, 288, 295, 373-4. ONS 72, ONS 73 / RNS 51, ONS 74-6, ONS 79-80, ONS 82 / RNS 53, ONS 83 / RNS 4, ONS 84 / RNS 54, ONS 85 / RNS 55, ONS 86. Cylinders 81, 82, 84.

Sam Gregory

Samuel Gregory is listed in the 1881 census as a shepherd, aged 49, living at Lob Gate, Pilsdon, with his wife Susan (49); sons Thomas (16), an agricultural labourer, Frank (8), and Samuel (6); and daughter Emma (12). The family was from Askerswell. In 1901 Sam and Susan are at East Street, Beaminster; they are both of 'undefined employment status'.

References:

FSJ III (11) 1907 77-8, 102. FSJ VII (27) 1923 46-7, 48-9, 51-4. PFD 69-70. PMB 4. PWS 101-2. REC 111, 230-1.

Broadwood Collection LEB/5/197, 199. Hammond Collection D523-37.

Mr Harper

A fisherman of King's Lynn, according to RVW. The 1901 census lists one fisherman by the name of Harper in the area: William (71), born at Lynn. He is living at Watsons Yard, King's Lynn, with his wife Sarah (58), and their adopted son Frederick Simmons (7). The North End at Lynn was the fishermen's quarter, and quite a separate community; its inhabitants, much intermarried, referred to other Lynn people as 'foreigners', and RVW wondered if they might be of Scandinavian ancestry. Most of the area was demolished during slum clearances in the 1930s.

References:

FSJ II 82-3, 162, 173. Bronson IV 250.7. PRVW 93-5. Vaughan Williams MSS III 196, 198, 200, 202, 204, 206, 208, 240, 242.

On RVW and the Lynn fishermen: 'Edgar Smith, Vaughan Williams and King's Lynn', ED&S 34 (3) 1972 92-6 and Elizabeth James, 'James Carter, Fisherman of King's Lynn', ED&S 39 (1) 1977 10-11.

Mr Harwood

For reference, see notes, *The Ship in Distress*.

Shadrack 'Shepherd' Hayden

Shadrack (Shadrach, Shadrick) Hayden (Haden) was born in Lyford, Berkshire, in 1829; his father was an agricultural labourer. In the 1881 census he is 52, living at Lodge Farm Cottages, Pusey, Buckinghamshire, and is working as a shepherd. His wife Jane is 67, and they have one daughter, Annie Wil(t)shire (27) and three grandchildren, Harry (5), Albert (3) and Edith (1) living with them, as well as two lodgers. In 1901 he is at Weald, Bampton (having moved there in the 1880s), 'living on own means'. Jane is listed as being 75, so we may assume an error in the 1881 transcription. Harry, now a mason's labourer, is still living with them, with his wife Charlotte. Sharp met 'Shepherd' through his Morris contacts at Bampton, and visited him a number of times, noting a total of 27 songs; Alfred Williams also got a few from him. 'Shepherd' Hayden died in 1916, active till the end, though a little deaf. In the 1930s, James Madison Carpenter noted several songs – including *John Barleycorn* – from Harry Wiltshire, still living at Weald. He had learned them all from his grandfather.

References:

Still Growing 49-50.

FSJ IV (17) 1913 326. FSJ V (18) 1914 62, 65, 73, 94. FSJ VIII (31) 1927 27, 41-2.

Bronson I 53.59; III 200.71; IV 279.36. KCSC I 49, 168-9, 205-6, 274-5, 288, 345, 351, 377-8, 672-3. KCSC II 3, 35-8, 90, 123, 177-8, 196-7, 239-40, 307, 338-9. WUP 120-1, 147-9, 162-3.

Sharp Collection: Folk Tunes 2289-91, 2308-12, 2332-5, 2365-71, 2381, 2388-91, 2431-3, 2941-2. Folk Words 2096-8, 2103-11, 2122-31, 2138-45, 2157-64.

Carpenter Collection: AFC 1972/001, MS pp. 00194-5, 00526-7, 00538-9, 00574-6, 00924-5, 05148-9, 07162, 08341-2 (Harry Wiltshire).

James Herridge

Described by E. T. Sweeting as 'labourer, aged 67'. The 1901 census lists no Herridges at Twyford, but there is a James Herage, 61, a railway platelayer. In 1881 he is living at Stiffs Lane, Twyford, with his wife Louisa (38); sons Edwin (15), a carter, and Frank (3); daughters Mabel (8), and Fanny (5), and a lodger, James Young, a retired labourer. In 1901, James and Louisa are at Park Lane, Twyford, with sons Harbert (19), a groom, and Walter (13); a grandson, Leonard (7); and a boarder, Ernest Dumper (28), a bricklayer.

References:

FSJ III (10) 1907 47-8. Bronson IV 289.36. PBC 127-8.

Henry Hills

Henry Hills was born in the early 1830s at Lodsworth, a village between Midhurst and Petworth in Sussex, where his parents kept a farm. Following his father's death in 1863, he took a farm on Black Down, a few miles to the north. After some fifteen years there, he occupied various other farms in Sussex and Surrey, until 1899 when he moved to Shepperton, where he met W. Percy Merrick. Between then and his death in the autumn of 1901, he sang a large number of songs for Merrick, some 57 of which, including toasts and drinking-game songs from harvest-home suppers, were printed in the *Journal*. He had known even more in his youth, some learned from family, many from carters around Lodsworth. He told Merrick:

'The carters always used to be at it when they were along with their horses … Just take up a stone and rattle it on the handle of the plough and sing to them, and the horses would go along as pretty and as well as possible. I almost feel as if I could go to plough and sing away now! We used to have a carter-chap living in the house, and he could sing scores of songs; sometimes of an evening we would sit up and sing for ever so long – first one would get hold of a ballad, and then another would get hold of a ballad, and so on. Sometimes a friend would come to stay with us from London or somewhere else, and if he could sing a song that I liked I would get him to sing it over until I learned it. I used to hear a lot of songs, too, at harvest-homes, tithe-feasts, rent-dinners, rabbit-hunts, and one place or another. Some of the farmers and men about there could sing out-and-out well – capital, they could.'

References:

FSJ I (3) 1901 64-138; FSJ I (4) 1902 220; FSJ I (5) 1904 268-276. FSJ II (7) 1905 83.

Bronson I 2.53, 7.9 (appendix); II 78.22, 84.3, 92.5 (appendix), 105.9; IV 286.27. Broadwood Collection LEB/5/298-318.

Mr Hilton

References:

FSJ IV (14) 1910 84, 87. FSJ IV (15) 1910 123. Bronson I 4.39; IV 283.17, 287.4. PECS 194-6. PRVW 104-76.

Broadwood Collection LEB/5/236.

Vaughan Williams MSS I 137, 139,140; 4to I 45 (1-5), 46 (1-5).

Louie (Louisa) Hooper and Lucy White

These two sisters provided Cecil Sharp with more than a hundred songs between them, sung individually and together, out of a varied repertoire of some three hundred. Their mother, Mrs Sarah England, had been a well-known local singer, and a lot of people in the district had learned songs from her. The sisters both worked as 'outworker' shirt-makers. In the 1901 census, Louie is a widow aged 40, with a daughter, Flossie (15) and a son, Archie (8); while Lucy is 53, living with her husband John (54), an agricultural engine driver, and sons John (27) and Nathaniel (17), both agricultural labourers, and daughters Bessie (19), Polly (15) and Maud (13), all shirt and buttonhole makers. Daughters Minnie, Adelina and Annie, and son Edward, who appear at Westport Row, Isle Brewers, in the 1881 census, are no longer living with them. In 1881, Louie was single, living at Ilminster Road, Puckington, with her parents, William and Sarah, and a younger brother, George. The women are listed as buttonhole workers, the men as agricultural labourers.

The sisters were both very musical, and Sharp spoke highly of their singing. Louie was a musician as well; Sharp once gave her a concertina. As a child she would lie in bed listening to the rain pattering on the roof. 'It would always turn itself into a little song. I was always full of music', she said. Lucy's *The False Bride* was, Sharp reckoned, the finest song he collected, bar one. In later life, Louie recalled

Sharp's visits with pleasure: 'I often think of the days,' she wrote. 'It was a happy time.' Lucy died in 1924 after a long illness; Louie died in 1946, and is buried in Hambridge churchyard. In 1942 the BBC recorded some songs from her, copies of which are held at the Vaughan Williams Memorial Library.

References:

Louie:

Still Growing 53-55.

FSJ II (6) 1905 15-16, 29, 37, 39. FSJ V (20) 1916 283-4.

Bronson I 12.35; II 65.9, 84.1; IV 279.25. SFS I: 6-7, 20-1, 34-7, 44-5, 48-54, 59, 62, 65-6, 68-71. KCSC I: 19, 29-30, 68, 102, 138, 203, 622, 697, 699-700. KCSC II: 30, 387, 405. RIP 82, 125, 179-80. SFS II: 10-11, 16-17, 40-1, 50-3.

Sharp Collection: Folk Tunes 5, 49, 55, 88-90, 101-3, 132-9, 191-2, 196, 265, 319, 320, 322, 324-6. Folk Words 10, 75, 83-4, 91, 94, 97-8, 100, 110-11, 207-12, 283-6, 288-9, 291-2, 432-3, 445-6, 448-50, 899, 900.

BBC Recordings 4014-5, 4039.

Lucy:

Still Growing 92-6.

FSJ II (6) 1905 5, 7, 10, 12-13, 27-8. FSJ VIII (31) 1927 4, 23-4.

Bronson I 4.71, 12.5 (appendix), 43.18; II 78.40, 92.20 (appendix), 112.16; III 209.9; IV 250.36. SFS I 8-9, 28-9, 32-3, 40-1, 59-60, 63-5. KCSC I 112, 175, 249, 267, 331, 401, 416, 426, 553-4, 633-4, 665, 691-2. KCSC II 21, 52, 109, 256-7, 269-70, 391-2, 594, 601. SFS II 4-9. RIP 110, 128.

Sharp Collection: Folk Tunes 75-6, 166-7, 189, 190, 194-5, 197, 220-22, 267-71, 317-8, 321, 323, 384, 504-8, 510-11, 518-20, 601-2, 646, 690, 850-1. Folk Words 106, 112, 254-5, 287, 290-1, 293-4, 308, 310, 375-7, 430-1, 444, 447, 512, 590-1, 692, 715, 765.

Both:

Maud Karpeles, *Cecil Sharp: His Life and Work* (1967 edn.) 32-3, 38.

FSJ II (6) 1905 10-11, 21-2, 33, 40, 51-2, 59.

Bronson I 24.17, 44.2 (appendix); II 112.18; IV 283.13. KCSC I 235, 294-5, 382-3, 430, 473-4, 678-9. KCSC II: 45-6, 67-8, 94-5, 150, 312. RIP 68, 119, 198-9, 238-9.

Sharp Collection: Folk Tunes 3, 6-12, 14-16, 19-21, 24-7, 34, 38-9, 50-4, 63-6, 77-9. Folk Words 3-5, 11-22, 25-7, 31-5, 41-6, 63-4, 69-71, 81-2, 85-90, 92-3, 105, 286.

Betty Howard

'Aged about 70' in January 1905, according to RVW. Perhaps Elizabeth Howard of King's Lynn, who appears in the 1901 census, aged 75, her occupation described as 'home duties', with a four year old boarder, Julia Norton.

References:

FSJ II (8) 1906 169-70, 172. PRVW 103-4. Vaughan Williams MSS III 212, 214, 216.

Christopher Jay

RVW met Mr Jay at the Bridge Inn at Acle. The 1901 census lists a Christopher Jay (48), labourer. In 1881 he is a general labourer (unemployed) living with his wife Ellen Emma (26) and son James (4 months); in 1901 he and Ellen Emma are at Causeway, Acle Bridge, with son Frederick (15) and daughter Sarah Elizabeth (10).

References:

FSJ IV (14) 1910 87, 90. PECS 120-1, 174-5.

Vaughan Williams MSS 4to I 32(1), 36(2), 37(1,2), 44(1-4).

Emily Joiner

Born Emily East on 25 April 1855 in the Union workhouse at Hemel Hempstead, Hertfordshire, Emily was educated in a 'plaiting school' kept by her great-grandmother (Sarah Hawkins, from whom many of her songs came) and grandmother, at Leverstock Green. The children learned to read and to plait straw for hats. Straw-plaiting was an important source of family income at a time when agricultural wages were low, but, by the end on the nineteenth century, cheap imports from the Far East had killed the industry. Emily married James Joiner, an agricultural labourer, in 1874; she already had a son, William How(e), baptised the previous year. By the time Lucy Broadwood and her niece Janet Broadwood noted this and other songs from Mrs Joiner, she was a widow (James had died in 1905) aged 59, doing odd gardening jobs. She sang 'with very great rhythmical feeling and purity of musical intervals, whilst choosing a much slower pace and a more deliberate and expressive phrasing than ... usually adopted by ... English country singers.' In the 1901 census, Emily, aged 45, and her husband James, 48, 'Working on Road', appear on the same page as the Broadwoods of Bone Hill. Janet was 5 at the time, the youngest of four children; her father was Henry Broadwood, 'Pianoforte Maker', and her family, by contrast, had three live-in servants.

In later life 'Aunt Em', as she became known, was Chiswell Green's unofficial midwife and layer-out, and local people generally tried her home-made remedies before spending money on a doctor. She invariably wore a black dress and bonnet, and, after her lodger Alf Gibbs died, lived alone in considerable poverty. She died of a stroke in 1938.

References:

Unpublished research by Alison Macfarlane of St Albans.

FSJ V (19) 1915 123-6, 128, 130, 159-62, 184-5, 190-1, 193-5, 197. Bronson II 73.8.

Broadwood Collection LEB/2/46-55.

Mr Kemp

Described by Walter Ford (1907) as an 'agricultural labourer, aged about 75'. The only male Kemp listed at Elstead in the 1901 census is George Kemp (86), general labourer. In 1881 he was living there with his wife Hannah (64), son George (24), grandson Alfred (12), and lodger George Woolgar (48). The men were all listed as agricultural labourers. In 1901, George is living at Sandford, Elstead, with daughter-in-law Alice (37) and her daughter Dorothy (11 months), nephew Arthur Linegar (21), a general labourer, and niece Annie Linegar (13).

References:

FSJ V (19) 1915 122-3, 154-5. Bronson I 12.25.

Elizabeth Lock

In the 1881 census, Elizabeth Lock (40) is living at 'Cottage', Muchelney Ham, with her husband George, a labourer, and they have a sister-in-law, Jane Hodder (33, a glover) living with them. They were all born locally. By the 1901 census, George has become a tenant farmer and employer. Between April 1904 and September 1905, Elizabeth sang more than 20 songs for Sharp. She died in 1915 after a fall in which she broke her thigh.

References:

Still Growing 56-7.

FSJ II (6) 1905 22-3, 25-6, 40-1.

Bronson I 12.45, 44.7; II 92.19 (appendix); IV 295.7. KCSC I 26, 220-1, 433, 510, 535, 538. KCSC II 76, 136, 228-229, 330. RIP 119. SFS I 22-3, 42-3, 62, 68.

Sharp Collection: Folk Tunes 159-64, 185-8, 253-9, 452-4, 498, 546, 645. Folk Words 243-9, 273-6, 351-2, 361-5, 615, 714.

Mr Locke

References:

FSJ IV (14) 1910 85-6, 132, 334. PRVW 110-13. Vaughan Williams MSS I 141, 142(1,2), 143, 144, 145, 452(1,2), 453, 454(1,2), 455.

Moses Mansfield

Clive Carey (1912) and Iolo Williams and Frederick Keel (1913) visited Moses Mansfield 'aged 81, labourer', at Almshouse Common (or Cottages), Haslemere. The 1901 census shows a Moses Mansfield (72), 'worker', living at Killinghurst, Chiddingfold, with his wife Emily (64), and a boarder, William Denger (32), a carter.

References:

FSJ V (19) 1915 167-8. FSJ VI (21) 1918 17-18.

Mrs Moore

For reference, see notes, *When I Was Young*.

Charles Neville

Sharp met Charles Neville through the latter's son, Alfred, who had already sung him two songs. Charles provided fourteen, some a little boisterous; Sharp was unable at the time to print the words for his version of *The Boatsman and the Tailor* (Roud 570 Laws Q8), so he set the tune to *The Green Wedding* (Roud 93 Child 221) instead. In the 1881 census, Charles is a carter aged 31, living at 1 Town End Cottages, East Coker, with his wife Mary (34), a field worker; daughters Elizabeth (11), Effie (3) and Emma (10 months); and sons Henry (6), Walter (5) and Thomas (10 months). Elizabeth's surname is Young (her mother's maiden name). In 1901, Charles is a widower, working as a woodman; Walter (now using his middle name, Gilbert) and Effie are still unmarried. There are three younger children; Martha (19), William (18) and Alfred (15); Mary's mother, Emma Young (89) is also living with them. Gilbert and William are web weavers, while Alfred is a twine maker.

References:

Still Growing 62-3.

FSJ IV (17) 1913 333. FSJ V (20) 1916 258-9.

Bronson I 4.10; III 209.27. KCSC I 9,

176-7, 477-8, 617. KCSC II 1-2, 7-8, 110, 162-3, 406-7 (with Alfred).

Sharp Collection: Folk Tunes 1817-24, 1834-6, 1839-40. Folk Words 1666-75, 1677-9.

RIP 83-4. SFS V 13-15, 32-6, 40-2.

(Alfred Neville: Sharp Collection: Folk Words 1617-19. Folk Tunes 1780, 1838.)

Emma Overd

Cecil Sharp met Mrs Overd, a singer of some repute and with a large repertoire, at Langport in Somerset. He was staying with the local vicar, and had been warned that she lived 'in a mean street, inhabited by bad people'. Finding her with a group of women friends outside the local pub, he explained that he was looking for old songs and hoped that she might sing him some; 'whereupon ... she flung her arms around him and danced him around with the utmost vigour, shouting "Lor, girls, here's my beau come at last"'. At this point, the vicar and his daughter passed by. They were horrified, so Sharp told them to go away; they went. He subsequently noted 43 songs from Emma during some eleven visits over the following five years. She was an extrovert, sometimes melodramatic singer, given to table-thumping at moments of excitement. Other 'bad people' from Knapps Lane (Eliza Hutchings and her daughter Ellen Trott) also sang songs for Sharp; he seems to have got on famously with them.

In the 1881 census, Emma (43) is living at Week, Curry Rivel, with her husband William (48); they were both born in the village. There are five sons: Henry (19), William (15), Charles (13), Herbert (10), and Arthur (5); and one daughter,

Alice (8). The three elder boys are agricultural labourers like their father. In 1901, they are at Langport; Arthur is still living with them, now also an agricultural labourer. Three other sons are living locally, with their families: Henry is now a carter, William a general labourer, and Charles a railway packer. Emma Overd died in 1928.

References:

Still Growing 67-9. Maud Karpeles, *Cecil Sharp: His Life and Work* (1967 edn.) 40.

FSJ II (6) 1905 7, 11, 13, 27, 28, 34, 42, 48. FSJ IV (17) 1913 282.

Bronson I 10.89, 24.2, 43.2; II 78.20, 95.49, 105.26; III 200.73, 209.18.

KCSC I 32, 38-9, 119-19, 128, 160-1, 224, 273, 280-1, 302-3, 379, 422-3, 512, 542-3, 584, 610, 629-30, 635-6, 643, 659-60, 663-4, 668-9, 671-2. KCSC II 27-8, 61-2, 106, 192, 358, 371, 516-7.

SFS I 5, 18-19, 24-5, 58-9, 62-3. II 32-3. III 12-13. V 54-5. PBB 117-18. RIP 106-8, 125-6, 129-30, 144, 159-60, 165-7, 181-2.

Sharp Collection: Folk Tunes 240-1, 245-8, 262-4, 292-7, 308-14, 327-8, 330-32, 341-3, 346, 379-81, 440-3, 2033, 2035. Folk Words 332-4, 342-7, 371-4, 394-402, 417-29, 453-60, 469-71, 473-4, 508-10, 555-60, 878, 1902-4, 1907.

Anna Pond

In the 1901 census, Anna Pond is 28 years old, living at 1, Pound Cottage, Shepton Beauchamp, with her husband Arthur (27), a farm carter; their sons Leonard (4), and Harold (3); and her father Joseph Cornelius, an agricultural labourer aged 68. They were all born locally. Anna is working at home as a glove machinist. There are a number of Pond and Cornelius women living in the area, the majority also working in the gloving trade. The 1881 census shows Joseph working as a shepherd and his wife Sarah as a glover, while Arthur's parents William and Lavinia are, respectively, an agricultural labourer and a glove sewer.

References:

FSJ II (6) 1905 8, 30-1, 109

Bronson I 12.91; II 73.76, 78.26; III 200.55. KCSC I 17-18, 72, 90, 165-6, 548. KCSC II 96-7. SFS 30-1.

Sharp Collection (VWML) Folk Words 406-11, 520-5. Folk Tunes 300-3, 390-3, 459.

Ellen Powell

References:

FSJ IV (15) 1910 114-5; (17) 1913 280. FSJ VIII (34) 1930 208.

Bronson I 344. Ella Leather, *Folk-Lore of Herefordshire*, 1912 202-3, 205. PRVW 74-7.

Broadwood Collection LEB/5/260, 262, 265, 278. Vaughan Williams MSS I 286(1,2), 287(1-3), 288(1,2), 289(1,2), 290(1-3), 291(2). Scrapbook p.57.

Dean Robinson

Born at Barnetby le Wold, Lincoln, Dean Robinson is listed in the 1881 census as a shoemaker, 47, living at Back Street, North Kelsey. His wife Emma is 40, and they have three sons: George (10), Thomas (6) and John (6 months). In 1901 they are living at Scawby Brook; Dean is still a self-employed shoemaker

working from home. George and John are unmarried and still living with them; George is a houseman on a farm, John is an engine fitter. There is a grandson, Jessie (15), working as a milk dealer's boy, and a visitor, Sarah Norton (19), who works in a sweet factory. Grainger noted eight songs from Mr Robinson, including a version of *Six Dukes*.

References:

FSJ II (7) 1905 79. FSJ III (10) 1908 174. Bronson III 140.5,6.

Broadwood Collection LEB/5/236. Grainger Collection (O'Brien Index) 105, 126, 180, 188, 285. ONS 58 / RNS 50, ONS 64-66, ONS 52 / RNS 49, RNS 84. Cylinders 131 and 132.

Marina Russell

Marina Russell was born in Corscombe in 1833, the daughter of stonemason James Sartin. The family were of Huguenot extraction, a John Sartin having moved to Dorset from Wiltshire in 1656. Marina worked in the glove-making trade, as did many of her female relatives, until her marriage in 1855 to Charles Russell, a farm labourer; she lived at Upwey from 1871, and brought up eleven children and an illegitimate grandchild. In the 1881 census she is a widow, working as a charwoman, living at Ridgeway Hamlet, Upwey, with her daughter Lavenia (20, a housemaid); sons Fred (14, a dairy boy), Samuel (10) and Walter (7); and grandson Alfred (5). In the 1901 census she is listed as a glover of undefined employment status, living alone. Her cousin Edith Sartin of Corscombe, from whom the Hammond brothers noted 11 songs, probably put them in touch with her, and altogether she sang 100 songs for them. Many were fragmentary – she was elderly by then and had perhaps forgotten quite a lot – and many had unusual tunes; she seems to have been particularly keen on the Dorian mode. On their second visit to her, in December 1907, Henry noticed that her singing was more uncertain than before, and that she showed a tendency to sound flat on the higher notes; he noted against one song, 'I think Mrs R must have sung C sharp here when she was in full control of her faculties and teeth'. She died in 1908.

References:

Unpublished research by Bonny Sartin of Sherborne.

Frank Purslow, *The Hammond Brothers' Song Collection* (FMJ 1 (4) 1968 236-266)

FSJ III (11) 1907 67-70, 78-9, 81, 84-5, 92, 99-111, 108, 111, 116-7, 119-20, 127, 129-30. FSJ IV (17) 1913 327.

FSJ VIII (34) 1930 188-90, 201-2, 209-11, 215-7. FMJ 1 (4) 1968 262; (5) 1969 308-9.

Bronson I 12.3 (appendix), 20.9, 43.19; III 170.2, 243.82; IV (Addenda) 78.1.2, 105.11.1. PCL 74. PFD 60, 62, 78, 87, 93-4, 97-100. PMB 59. PWS 28, 39, 59, 73, 78.

Hammond Collection D755-836, D890-907.

Charles Spiller

In the 1881 census, Charles Spiller (55) is farming the 180 acres of Kibbier *(sic)* Farm – with one employee – at Pitminster in Dorset. His wife Mary is 48, and they have six daughters: Elizabeth (28), Charlotte (21), Jessie (20, a schoolmistress), Mary (12),

Petronella (10), and Laura (4); and four sons: Charles (18), William (16), Edward (14), and George (8). He may only recently have taken over the farm; in the *Post Office Directory of Somerset and Bristol* (1875) he is listed as a dairyman. By 1901 Charles is retired, and a widower. He is still at Kibbear House Farm, which is now being run by Edward and George; both, like their sisters Petronella and Laura, unmarried.

References:

FSJ V (20) 1916 260-1. Bronson IV 277.35. KCSC I 197. Sharp Collection: Folk Tunes 1815. Folk Words 1658-9.

Henry Stansbridge

Aged 58 in 1906, according to Gardiner. He seems to have been born in 1848 or 1849; in 1873 he married Fanny Blake of Lyndhurst, Hampshire (daughter of George Blake, from whom Gardiner also noted songs), and by 1888 they had three children: Harry, Frances and Frank. At the time of the 1881 census, Harry (2) is staying with his uncle and aunt, Frederick and Maria Grey, at Gosport Street, Lymington; there is no sign locally of his parents in this or in the 1901 census, but Henry at least must have been in Lyndhurst in 1905.

References:

Unattributed genealogical data, Church of Jesus Christ of Latter-day Saints.

FSJ III (13) 1909 253-4, 284-5, 301-2. Bronson II 85.24. PCL 15-16, 50. REC 256.

Gardiner Collection H412, H414, and two other songs.

John Stickle

John Stickle was born in March 1875 and worked as a cooper, first at Baltasound on Unst and later in Lerwick, making barrels for the herring trade. In his spare time he was much in demand as a fiddler for local dances and weddings, and as a singer and reciter at concerts. His great-great grandfather, Friedemann von Stickel, had been a German who was shipwrecked on Unst some time around the 1770s (clutching his fiddle, according to local legend) and who settled in the area, marrying a woman from Unst and, after her death, a woman from Yell. His son, also Friedemann (born in the 1780s), was a fiddler of some repute and a number of tunes attributed to him, such as *Da Trowie Burn*, are still played in Shetland. His son Robert passed on the family's musicality and repertoire (and his violin) to his grandson John.

Patrick Shuldham-Shaw, who first met John in 1946, described him as 'a great character. Like most Shetlanders he had a wonderful sense of humour and was particularly fond of pulling one's leg. There was never any malice in his fun and he was hospitable and kind to a fault and a truly loyal friend. He was shortish and thickset with a big moustache for which he was sometimes nicknamed Stalin.'

His playing had a particularly lyrical quality and his stock of tunes, about which he was often very knowledgeable, was large; Shuldham-Shaw noted 92 items from him. Beside singing *When I Was a Little Boy*, he caused some amazement by producing a fragment of the very rare ballad *King Orfeo* (Roud 136 Child 19). The only example known to Child – perhaps descended from the mediaeval romance – was also from Unst, and John's tune is the only one ever recorded for it. He died in 1957.

References:

Patrick Shuldham-Shaw: *A Shetland Fiddler and His Repertoire: John Stickle, 1875-1957*, JEFDSS IX (3) 1962 129-147; *Folk Music and Dance in Shetland*, JEFDSS V (2) 1947 74-80; *Folk Songs Collected in the Shetland Isles*, JEFDSS VI (1) 1949 13-18. Bronson I 19.

Various recordings of John Stickle are currently available from Folktrax (see bibliography).

Joseph Taunton

In the 1881 census, Joseph is 42, an unmarried general labourer, living at the family home at Farmers End, Corscombe, Dorset. Head of the household is his mother Jane (66), an unmarried farm servant; her sister Grace (54), a glover, also lives with them, together with Joseph's sister Elizabeth Ann (22), also a glover, and brother Alfred (17), a general labourer. In 1901 Joseph is still unmarried and living at Farmers End with his Aunt Grace acting as housekeeper.

References:

FSJ IV (17) 1913 303. FSJ III 93-5, 121-2. FSJ VII (27)1923 77, 83, 91. Bronson IV 250.34. PCL 68-9.

Broadwood Collection LEB/5/207. Hammond Collection: D611-19, D842-56.

John Trump

In 1881, John Trump (47) is living at Back Lane, North Petherton, Somerset, with his wife Jane (48), and sons Frederick (18), a general labourer like his father, and Samuel (6). In 1901, John, Jane and Samuel are at High Street; John's employment status is 'undefined', while Samuel is working as a butcher's assistant.

References:

FSJ V (20) 1916 284. Bronson I 4.54. KCSC I 289, 486. KCSC II 171-2, 437-8.

Sharp Collection: Folk Tunes 902-5. Folk Words 976-7.

Mrs Vaisey

Lucy Broadwood met Mrs Vaisey, 'a gardener's wife, a native of Hampshire' at Adwell, Oxfordshire, in 1892. 'Mrs Vaisey', she wrote, 'knew numbers of excellent old songs. When I expressed a hope that her children would learn them she said, 'They like to pick them up from me, and I like the old ballads myself, but my husband he says, Don't teach them that rubbish! Give them *Hymns Ancient and Modern*!'"

References:

FSJ I (4) 1902 224-5. FSJ I (5) 1904 266-7. FSJ IV (15) 1910 124, 127-8. Bronson II 84.23.

Broadwood Collection LEB/2/66-68.

Harriet and Peter Verrall

Harriet Verrall was born at Slaugham, Sussex, around 1855, and her husband Peter, an agricultural labourer, at Lewes a year or so earlier. In the 1881 census they are living with her parents, Richard and Amelia Richardson, at 5 Crossways Cottages, Lower Beeding. In the 1901 census, they are at or near Nuthurst (address unrecorded, but most of the neighbours are at 'Thrift Cottages'); Richard, aged 77 and still working as an agricultural labourer, is listed as head of the household; Amelia has died. There are two granddaughters: Ellen (19), and Alice (17); and two grandsons: Frederick (11), and Arthur (7 months); presumably these are all Harriet and Peter's children. There is also a two-year old niece of Richard's, Ethel Holland.

In 1904, their address was Nuthurst Road, Monk's Gate, and on 24 May, Vaughan Williams noted eight songs from Harriet. In all, he got 48 songs from the Verralls over the next four years (though he often neglected the words); 24 from Harriet and 3 from Peter; the other 21 they sang together. In late 1904, the *West Sussex Gazette* announced a competition for 'old songs'; Lucy Broadwood judged the 'words and music' section, and Harriet won prizes for her *Salisbury Plain* (q.v.) and *Covent Garden* (Roud 903 Laws M12: see FSJ II (8) 1906 195-6).

In about 1905 the Verralls moved to 34 North Street, Horsham, and later to Stanley Street. George Butterworth and Francis Jekyll also noted some songs from them. Harriet's *Our Captain Calls* (Roud 602: see FSJ II (8) 1906 202) provided the tune to which RVW set Bunyan's poem *He Who Would Valiant Be* (as modified by Percy Dearmer, 1906), and the melody is referred to in hymnals as *Monk's Gate*. Harriet died in 1918, aged about 63, and was buried in an unmarked grave in Hill's Cemetery, Horsham. Peter died a few years later. There is a recording which is probably of him, singing *The Rambling Sailor* (Roud 518), on *A Century of Song*.

References:

Stanley Godman, *The 'West Sussex Gazette'
Song Competition of 1904*, JEFDSS IX (4)
1964 269-273.

FSJ II: (7) 1905 98, 118, 127; (8) 1906
156, 194-202, 208. FSJ IV: (14) 1910
121; (17) 1913 279, 281, 284, 302, 327,
337.

Bronson I 4.12; IV 250.12, (Addenda)
43.10.1. DPG: 36-7, 43. PBB 229-31.
PECS 74-5, 92-3, 171-2. PRVW; 8
songs, 157-168, notes 199-200.

Michael Kennedy, *The Works of Ralph
VaughanWilliams*. Oxford 1964, Appendix
Two: *Folk Songs Collected by Vaughan
Williams*.

Vaughan Williams MSS: I   234, 236,
238(1,2), 260, 261, 262(1,2), 263-5,
401, 402; II   138, 140, 142, 144, 146,
148, 150, 154, 252, 254, 256, 258, 260,
262, 264, 266, 268, 270, 272, 274, 338,
340, 342, 344-350; III   289, 291, 293,
295, 297, 299, 421-3, 425.

SELECT BIBLIOGRAPHY

This listing replaces that provided by Vaughan Williams and Lloyd in 1959. A bibliography including a wider range of song collections is available on the EFDSS website at http://www.efdss.org/

STANDARD REFERENCE WORKS

Bronson, Bertrand Harris, *The Traditional Tunes of the Child Ballads, With Their Texts, According to the Extant Records of Great Britain and America*, 4 vols (Princeton: Princeton University Press, 1959–72).

Chappell, W[illiam], *Popular Music of the Olden Time: A Collection of Ancient Songs, Ballads, and Dance Tunes, Illustrative of the National Music of England. With Short Introductions to the Different Reigns, and Notices of the Airs from Writers of the Sixteenth and Seventeenth Centuries. Also a Short Account of the Minstrels*, Airs harmonized by G. A Macfarren, 2 vols (London: Cramer, Beale and Chappell, [1855–59]; reprinted with a new Introduction by Frederick W. Sternfeld, New York: Dover, 1965). Also appears under the title *The Ballad Literature and Popular Music of the Olden Time* ...

Child, Francis James, ed. *The English and Scottish Popular Ballads*, 5 vols (Boston: Houghton, Mifflin, 1882–98; reprinted New York: Dover, 1965). A revised edition (with the additions and corrections incorporated into the body of the text and tunes added) is in the process of publication by Loomis House Press; a CD-ROM version is published by Heritage Muse.

Coffin, Tristram Potter, *The British Traditional Ballad in North America*, revised edn. with a supplement by Roger de V.

Renwick, Bibliographical and Special Series published through the cooperation of the American Folklore Society (Austin: University of Texas Press, 1977).

Dean-Smith, Margaret, *A Guide to English Folk Song Collections 1822–1952, With an Index to Their Contents, Historical Annotations and an Introduction* (Liverpool: University Press of Liverpool in association with the English Folk Dance and Song Society, 1954). Standard guide to the contents and often convoluted publishing history of early printed folk song collections.

Journal of the Folk-Song Society (1899–1931); *Journal of the English Folk Dance and Song Society* (1932–64); *Folk Music Journal* (1965–).

Laws, G. Malcolm, Jr, *American Balladry from British Broadsides: A Guide for Students and Collectors of Traditional Song*, Publications of the American Folklore Society, Bibliographical and Special Series, Vol. 8 (Philadelphia: American Folklore Society, 1957); *Native American Balladry: A Descriptive Study and a Bibliographical Syllabus*, revised edn, Publications of the American Folklore Society, Bibliographical and Special Series, Vol. 1 (Philadelphia: American Folklore Society, 1964).

Roud, Steve, *Broadside Index* and *Folk Song Index*, electronic indexes on CD-ROM, regularly updated (available for consultation in the Vaughan Williams Memorial Library or on subscription from Southwood, High Street, Maresfield, East Sussex TN22 2EH).

Simpson, Claude M., *The British Broadside Ballad and Its Music* (New Brunswick: Rutgers University Press, 1966).

FOLK SONG AND BALLAD STUDIES

This list includes mostly books, with just a few key articles; regrettably some are out of print and difficult to obtain, but can still be consulted in libraries.

Andersen, Flemming G., Otto Holzapfel, and Thomas Pettitt, *The Ballad as Narrative: Studies in the Ballad Traditions of England, Scotland, Germany and Denmark* (Odense: Odense University Press, 1982).

Andersen, Flemming G., *Commonplace and Creativity: The Role of Formulaic Diction in Anglo-Scottish Traditional Balladry*, Odense University Studies from the Medieval Centre, Vol. 1 (Odense: Odense University Press, 1985).

Atkinson, David, *The English Traditional Ballad: Theory, Method, and Practice* (Aldershot and Burlington, VT: Ashgate, 2002).

Bohlman, Philip V., *The Study of Folk Music in the Modern World*, Folkloristics (Bloomington and Indianapolis: Indiana University Press, 1988).

Bronson, Bertrand Harris, *The Ballad as Song* (Berkeley and Los Angeles: University of California Press, 1969). A collection of Bronson's articles.

Buchan, David, *The Ballad and the Folk* (London: Routledge & Kegan Paul, 1972; reprinted with Foreword by Ian A. Olson, Phantassie: Tuckwell Press, 1997). Exclusively concerned with Scottish ballads, but historically a key work for its methodology.

Cheesman, Tom, and Sigrid Rieuwerts, eds, *Ballads into Books: The Legacies of Francis James Child*, Selected Papers from the 26th International Ballad Conference (SIEF Ballad Commission), Swansea, Wales, 19–24 July 1996 (Bern: Peter Lang, 1997). A collection of essays, including quite an extensive bibliography of ballad studies.

Dugaw, Dianne, *Warrior Women and Popular Balladry, 1650–1850*, Cambridge Studies in Eighteenth-Century English Literature and Thought, 4 (Cambridge: Cambridge University Press, 1989; reprinted with a new Preface, Chicago and London: University of Chicago Press, 1996).

Dunn, Ginette, *The Fellowship of Song: Popular Singing Traditions in East Suffolk* (London: Croom Helm, 1980).

Elbourne, Roger, *Music and Tradition in Early Industrial Lancashire 1780–1840*, Mistletoe Series (Woodbridge: D. S. Brewer; Totowa, NJ: Rowman and Littlefield, for the Folklore Society, 1980).

Fowler, David C., *A Literary History of the Popular Ballad* (Durham, NC: Duke University Press, 1968). Especially good on the early history of ballad and folk song.

Friedman, Albert B., *The Ballad Revival: Studies in the Influence of Popular on Sophisticated Poetry* (Chicago: University of Chicago Press, 1961). Traces the development of literary interest in ballads and broadsides, and the history of ballad publications.

Gammon, Vic, 'Song, Sex, and Society in England, 1600–1850', *Folk Music Journal*, 4 (1982), 208–45. A key article on understanding folk song in historical context.

Gerould, Gordon Hall, *The Ballad of Tradition* (Oxford: Clarendon Press, 1932). Still a good introduction to ballads.

Hodgart, M. J. C., *The Ballads*, 2nd edn, Hutchinson University Library (London: Hutchinson, 1962). Highly readable, excellent short introduction to ballads.

Leach, MacEdward, and Tristram P. Coffin, eds, *The Critics & the Ballad* (Carbondale: Southern Illinois University Press, 1961). A collection of essays.

Lloyd, A. L., *The Singing Englishman: An Introduction to Folk Song* (London: Workers' Music Association, [1944]).

Lloyd, A. L., *Folk Song in England* (London: Lawrence and Wishart, 1967). Should be read in conjunction with Vic Gammon's essay on 'A. L. Lloyd and History' in Ian Russell, ed., *Singer, Song and Scholar*.

Lyle, E. B., ed., *Ballad Studies*, Mistletoe Series (Cambridge: D. S. Brewer; Totowa, NJ: Rowman and Littlefield, for the Folklore Society, 1976). A collection of essays.

McCarthy, William Bernard, *The Ballad Matrix: Personality, Milieu, and the Oral Tradition* (Bloomington and Indianapolis: Indiana University Press, 1990). Exclusively on Scottish material.

Palmer, Roy, *The Sound of History: Songs and Social Comment* (Oxford: Oxford University Press, 1988; reprinted London: Pimlico, 1996).

Pickering, Michael, *Village Song & Culture: A Study Based on the Blunt Collection of Song from Adderbury, North Oxfordshire* (London: Croom Helm, 1982).

Pickering, Michael, and Tony Green, eds, *Everyday Culture: Popular Song and the Vernacular Milieu*, Popular Music in Britain (Milton Keynes: Open University Press, 1987). A collection of essays.

Renwick, Roger deV., *English Folk Poetry: Structure and Meaning*, Publications of the American Folklore Society, New Series, Vol. 2 (Philadelphia: University of Pennsylvania Press, 1980).

Renwick, Roger deV., *Recentering Anglo/American Folksong: Sea Crabs and Wicked Youths* (Jackson: University Press of Mississippi, 2001).

Russell, Ian, ed., *Singer, Song and Scholar* (Sheffield: Sheffield Academic Press, 1986). A collection of essays.

Russell, Ian, 'Stability and Change in a Sheffield Singing Tradition', *Folk Music Journal*, 5 (1987), 317–58. An important counterweight to Sharp's *English Folk-Song: Some Conclusions*.

Russell, Ian, 'England (i), II: Traditional Music', in *The New Grove Dictionary of Music and Musicians*, ed. Stanley Sadie, executive editor John Tyrrell, 2nd edn, 29 vols (London: Macmillan, 2001), VIII, 227–39. An encyclopaedia article providing an excellent introduction to the subject.

Russell, Ian, and David Atkinson, eds, *Folk Song: Tradition, Revival, and Re-Creation*, Elphinstone Institute Occasional Publications, 3 (Aberdeen: Elphinstone Institute, University of Aberdeen, 2003). A collection of essays.

Sharp, Cecil J., *English Folk-Song: Some Conclusions* (London: Simpkin; Novello; Taunton: Barnicott & Pearce, 1907); 2nd edn, Preface by Maud Karpeles (London: Novello; Simpkin Marshall; Taunton: Barnicotts, 1936); 3rd edn, revised by Maud Karpeles, with an appreciation of Cecil Sharp by Ralph Vaughan Williams (London: Methuen, 1954); 4th edn, revised by Maud Karpeles, with an appreciation of Cecil Sharp by Ralph

Vaughan Williams (London: Mercury Books, 1965). Hastily written and much criticised, but still a foundation document of folk song studies; should be read in conjunction with Ian Russell's article on 'Stability and Change in a Sheffield Singing Tradition'.

Shields, Hugh, *Narrative Singing in Ireland: Lays, Ballads, Come-all-yes and Other Songs* (Blackrock: Irish Academic Press, 1993). Exclusively on Irish material.

Toelken, Barre, *Morning Dew and Roses: Nuance, Metaphor, and Meaning in Folksongs*, Folklore and Society, Publications of the American Folklore Society, New Series (Urbana and Chicago: University of Illinois Press, 1995).

Wilgus, D. K., *Anglo-American Folksong Scholarship Since 1898* (New Brunswick: Rutgers University Press, 1959). The standard account of early scholarship both sides of the Atlantic.

THE ENGLISH FOLK REVIVAL

This list reflects the currently vibrant interest in the study of the English folk revival(s), where the late twentieth-century revisionism of Harker and Boyes is now being challenged, so far mainly in articles.

Bearman, C. J., 'Who Were the Folk? The Demography of Cecil Sharp's Somerset Folk Singers', *Historical Journal*, 43 (2000), 751–75.

Bearman, Christopher James, 'The English Folk Music Movement 1898–1914', PhD thesis, University of Hull, 2001.

Bearman, C. J., 'Cecil Sharp in Somerset: Some Reflections on the Work of David

Harker', *Folklore*, 113 (2002), 11–34.

Boyes, Georgina, *The Imagined Village: Culture, Ideology and the English Folk Revival*, Music and Society (Manchester: Manchester University Press, 1993).

Fox Strangways, A. H., in collaboration with Maud Karpeles, *Cecil Sharp* (London: Oxford University Press, 1933); Fox Strangways, A. H., and Maud Karpeles, *Cecil Sharp*, 2nd edn. (London: Oxford University Press, 1955); Karpeles, Maud, *Cecil Sharp: His Life and Work* (London: Routledge & Kegan Paul, 1967). Effectively three editions of the only biography of Sharp to date.

Francmanis, John, 'National Music to National Redeemer: The Consolidation of a "Folk Song" Construct in Edwardian England', *Popular Music*, 21 (2002), 1–25.

Gammon, Vic, 'Folk Song Collecting in Sussex and Surrey, 1843–1914', *History Workshop Journal*, no. 10 (1980), 61–89.

Harker, Dave, *Fakesong: The Manufacture of British 'Folksong' 1700 to the Present Day*, Popular Music in Britain (Milton Keynes: Open University Press, 1985). Should be read in conjunction with Bearman's critiques.

Laing, Dave, Karl Dallas, Robin Denselow, and Robert Shelton, *The Electric Muse: The Story of Folk into Rock* (London: Eyre Methuen, 1975). Popular account of post-war developments.

Livingston, Tamara E., 'Music Revivals: Towards a General Theory', *Ethnomusicology*, 43 (1999), 66–85. A theoretical but accessible synthesis of characteristics of folk revivals internationally.

MacKinnon, Niall, *The British Folk Scene:*

Musical Performance and Social Identity, Popular Music in Britain (Buckingham: Open University Press, 1994). A sociological analysis of the post-war folk revival.

FOLK SONG COLLECTIONS

Very many song books have been published since the beginning of the revival of interest in English folk song; and large numbers of songs were also printed in the *Journal of the Folk-Song Society* and *Journal of the English Folk Dance and Song Society*. This list includes some of the more substantial publications, many of them regrettably out of print.

Baring-Gould, S., and H. Fleetwood Sheppard, *A Garland of Country Song: English Folk Songs with Their Traditional Melodies* (London: Methuen, 1895; reprinted with new Introduction by Martin Graebe, Felinfach: Llanerch, 1998).

Baring-Gould, S., H. Fleetwood Sheppard, and F. W. Bussell, *Songs of the West: Folk Songs of Devon & Cornwall Collected from the Mouths of the People*, new and revised edn. under the musical editorship of Cecil J. Sharp [3rd edn] (London: Methuen, [1905]). Some of the words retouched by Baring-Gould.

Broadwood, Lucy E., ed., *English Traditional Songs and Carols, With Annotations and Pianoforte Accompaniments* (London: Boosey, 1908).

Broadwood, Lucy E., and J. A. Fuller Maitland, eds, *English County Songs:Words and Music* (London: Leadenhall Press; J. B. Cramer; Simpkin, Marshall, Hamilton, Kent, 1893).

Bruce, J. Collingwood, and John Stokoe,

eds, *Northumbrian Minstrelsy: A Collection of the Ballads, Melodies, and Small-Pipe Tunes of Northumbria* (Newcastle-upon-Tyne: Society of Antiquaries of Newcastle-upon-Tyne, 1882; reprinted Felinfach: Llanerch, 1998).

Copper, Bob, *A Song for Every Season: A Hundred Years of a Sussex Farming Family* (London: Heinemann, 1971; reprinted [new edition] Peacehaven: Coppersongs, 1997). A good selection of songs, following a highly readable account of the rural Sussex background against which the Copper family sang them.

[Copper Family, The], *The Copper Family Song Book – A Living Tradition*, Introduction by Bob Copper, music transcription by David and Caro Kettlewell, music artwork by Bob Copper (Peacehaven: Coppersongs, 1995).

Deacon, George, *John Clare and the Folk Tradition* (London: Sinclair Browne, 1983; reprinted London: Francis Boutle, 2002).

Gardham, Steve, *An East Riding Songster:A Selection of Folk-Song from the East Riding*, musical arrangements by Dave Hill (Lincoln and Hull: Lincolnshire and Humberside Arts, 1982).

Hamer, Fred, *Garners Gay: English Folk Songs Collected by Fred Hamer* (London: E.F.D.S. Publications, 1967); *Green Groves: More English Folk Songs Collected by Fred Hamer* (London: E.F.D.S. Publications, 1973).

Holloway, John, and Joan Black, eds, *Later English Broadside Ballads*, 2 vols (London: Routledge & Kegan Paul, 1975–79). Texts only.

Hudleston, Mary and Nigel, *Songs of the Ridings:TheYorkshire Musical Museum*, transcribed, compiled, and annotated by

Mark Gordon and Richard Adams under the direction of Nigel A. Hudleston (Scarborough: G. A. Pindar and Son, 2001).

Karpeles, Maud, ed., *Cecil Sharp's Collection of English Folk Songs*, 2 vols (London: Oxford University Press, 1974). The largest selection of Sharp's English folk songs, but still disappointingly incomplete.

Karpeles, Maud, ed., *The Crystal Spring: English Folk Songs Collected by Cecil Sharp*, 2 vols (also in one vol.) (London: Oxford University Press, 1975).

Kennedy, Peter, ed., *Folksongs of Britain and Ireland: A Guidebook to the Living Tradition of Folksinging in the British Isles and Ireland, Containing 360 Folksongs from Field Recordings Sung in English, Lowland Scots, Scottish Gaelic, Irish Gaelic and Manx Gaelic, Welsh, Cornish, Channel Islands French, Romany and Tinkers' Cants, etc.* (London: Cassell, 1975; reprinted London: Oak/Music Sales, 1984).

Kidson, Frank, ed., *Traditional Tunes: A Collection of Ballad Airs, Chiefly Obtained in Yorkshire and the South of Scotland; Together with Their Appropriate Words from Broadsides and from Oral Tradition* (Oxford: Chas. Taphouse, 1891; rpt. East Ardsley: S.R. Publishers, 1970; Felinfach: Llanerch, 1999).

MacColl, Ewan, and Peggy Seeger, *Travellers' Songs from England and Scotland* (London: Routledge & Kegan Paul, 1977).

O'Shaughnessy, Patrick, ed., *Twenty-One Lincolnshire Folk-Songs from the Manuscript Collection of Percy Grainger* (London: Oxford University Press in conjunction with the Lincolnshire Association, 1968); *More Folk Songs from Lincolnshire* (London:

Oxford University Press in conjunction with the Lincolnshire Association, 1971); *Yellowbelly Ballads: A Third Selection of Lincolnshire Folk-Songs, the Majority of Them from the Collection of Percy Aldridge Grainger*, 2 pts (Lincoln: Lincolnshire and Humberside Arts, 1975); *Late Leaves from Lincolnshire: Folk-Songs Still in Oral Tradition There, Collected by Brian Dawson, John Pape & Patrick O'Shaughnessy* (Lincoln and Hull: Lincolnshire and Humberside Arts, 1980).

Palmer, Roy, ed., *Songs of the Midlands*, music editors Pamela Bishop and Katharine Thomson (East Ardsley: EP Publishing, 1972).

Palmer, Roy, ed., *Everyman's Book of English Country Songs* (London: Dent, 1979; reprinted as *English Country Songbook*, London: Omnibus Press, 1986).

Palmer, Roy, ed., *Everyman's Book of British Ballads* (London: Dent, 1980; reprinted as *A Book of British Ballads*, Felinfach: Llanerch, 1998).

Palmer, Roy, ed., *Folk Songs Collected by Ralph Vaughan Williams* (London: Dent, 1983; reprinted with corrections as *Bushes and Briars: Folk Songs Collected by Ralph Vaughan Williams*, Felinfach: Llanerch, 1999).

Palmer, Roy, *Boxing the Compass: Sea Songs & Shanties* (Todmorden: Herron Publishing, 2001). Revised and expanded edition of Roy Palmer, ed., *The Oxford Book of Sea Songs* (Oxford: Oxford University Press, 1986).

Pinto, Vivian de Sola, and Allan Edwin Rodway, eds, *The Common Muse: An Anthology of Popular British Ballad Poetry, XVth–XXth Century* (London: Chatto & Windus, 1957). Words only.

Purslow, Frank, ed., *Marrow Bones: English Folk Songs from the Hammond and Gardiner Mss.* (London: E.F.D.S. Publications, 1965); *The Wanton Seed: More English Folk Songs from the Hammond & Gardiner Mss.* (London: E.F.D.S. Publications, 1968); *The Constant Lovers: More English Folk Songs from the Hammond & Gardiner Mss.* (London: E.F.D.S. Publications, 1972); *The Foggy Dew: More English Folk Songs from the Hammond & Gardiner Mss.* (London: E.F.D.S. Publications, 1974).

Reeves, James, ed., *The Idiom of the People: English Traditional Verse, Edited with an Introduction and Notes from the Manuscripts of Cecil J. Sharp* (London: Heinemann, 1958); *The Everlasting Circle: English Traditional Verse, Edited with an Introduction and Notes from the Manuscripts of S. Baring-Gould, H. E. D. Hammond and George B. Gardiner* (London: Heinemann, 1960). Words only, with useful introductory essays.

Richards, Sam, and Tish Stubbs, *The English Folksinger: 159 Modern and Traditional Folksongs* (Glasgow and London: Collins, 1979). Includes some contemporary compositions.

Sharp, Cecil J., and Charles L. Marson, eds, *Folk Songs from Somerset*, 5 series [4th and 5th Series ed. Cecil J. Sharp] (London: Simpkin, Marshall, Hamilton, Kent / Simpkin; Schott; Taunton: Barnicott and Pearce, 1904–09).

Sharp, Cecil J., ed. *One Hundred English Folksongs* (Boston: Oliver Ditson, 1916; reprinted New York: Dover, 1975). US-published selection of songs collected by Sharp, listed as still in print; similar in content to *English Folk Songs*, Selected Edition.

Sharp, Cecil J., *English Folk Songs*, Selected Edition, 2 vols (London: Novello, [1920]; reprinted in one vol., 1959). Among Sharp's last publications; Cecil Sharp published very many song books (especially for schools) – see also the selections edited by Maud Karpeles.

Still Growing: English Traditional Songs and Singers from the Cecil Sharp Collection, ed. Steve Roud, Eddie Upton, and Malcolm Taylor (London: English Folk Dance & Song Society in association with Folk South West, 2003).

Stubbs, Ken, *The Life of a Man: English Folk Songs from the Home Counties Collected by Ken Stubbs*, material transcribed from tapes by Roger Nicholls (London: E.F.D.S. Publications, 1970).

Williams, Alfred, ed., *Folk-Songs of the Upper Thames, With an Essay on Folk-Song Activity in the Upper Thames Neighbourhood* (London: Duckworth, 1923; reprinted with a new Preface by Stewart F. Sanderson, East Ardsley: S. R. Publishers, [1968]). Words only.

SPECIALIST RECORD LABELS

Folktrax: http://www.folktrax.freeserve.co.uk/

Musical Traditions: http://www.mustrad.org.uk/records.htm

Topic: http://www.topicrecords.co.uk/

Veteran: http://www.oldhatmusic.freeserve.co.uk/

ONLINE RESOURCES

Bodleian Library Broadside Ballads

http://www.bodley.ox.ac.uk/ballads/ballads.htm

The Bodleian Library in Oxford holds a collection of over 30,000 printed ballads ranging from the sixteenth to the twentieth century; these are fully indexed in a searchable catalogue, and digitised copies can be viewed online.

British Library Traditional Music in England Project

http://www.bl.uk/collections/sound-archive/traditional_music.html

Online catalogues of collections of field recordings of traditional music in England held by the National Sound Archive, linked to their continuing digitisation project.

FARNE (Folk Archive Resource North East)

http://www.farneweblog.com/

Online archiving project concentrating on Northumbrian folk music which is gradually making available text, audio and photographic materials.

James Madison Carpenter Collection Online Catalogue

http://www.hrionline.ac.uk/carpenter/

A full catalogue of Carpenter's extensive collection, made between 1927 and 1955, of traditional song and drama from Britain, Ireland and the USA; eventually it is hoped to make the entire collection available online.

Max Hunter Folk Song Collection

http://www.smsu.edu/folksong/maxhunter/

Almost 1600 Ozark Mountain folk songs, recorded between 1956 and 1976, with texts, audio and staff notation; much of the material is of British origin, and a number of the songs in this book are represented, sometimes in multiple versions.

Mudcat Café: Digital Tradition Folk Song Database

http://www.mudcat.org/threads.cfm

Currently contains some 9000 song texts, an increasing number with tunes in MIDI format; the largest site of its kind, but material is submitted and processed by volunteers, and is of varying quality and accuracy, so should be used with caution. The site also hosts an extensive, fully archived discussion forum in which information may be sought, and questions asked and answered.

Musical Traditions

http://www.mustrad.org.uk/

An extensive magazine in digital format, which contains much of interest relating to traditional singing and revivals, including Keith Summers' 'Sing, Say, or Pay' (traditional music in Suffolk); Mike Brocken's thesis 'The British Folk Revival' (scheduled for publication as a book by Ashgate in late 2003); Mike Yates' 'Cecil Sharp in America'; full notes, reviews, and listings for Topic Records' *Voice of the People* series; traditional music discographies, and archive material.

Olson, Wm. Bruce. Roots of Folk: Old English, Scots, and Irish Songs and Tunes

http://users.erols.com/olsonw/

Densely organised and scholarly series of indexes of early broadside ballads, ballad operas and their tunes; includes tunes for sixteenth and seventeenth century broadsides in ABC format, systems for tune comparison, and examinations of the early history of various pieces. Contains a great deal of interest, particularly on the relationships of early printed sources and traditional music.

Traditional Song Forum

http://www.tradsong.freeserve.co.uk/

A group open to researchers, collectors and others with an interest in traditional song; the site contains a small but growing collection of articles and other resources, including a substantial guide to online resources at
http://www.tradsong.freeserve.co.uk/Websource.htm

Index of First Lines